Packet SwitchStream (PSS) – A User's Guide

J E Lane

PUBLISHED BY NCC PUBLICATIONS

British Library Cataloguing in Publication Data

Lane, J. E.
    Packet SwitchStream (PSS): a user's guide.
    1. Packet switching (Data transmission)
    I. Title
    001.64   TK5105
ISBN 0-85012-499-9

First published in 1987 by:

NCC Publications, The National Computing Centre Limited, Oxford Road, Manchester M1 7ED, England.

Typeset in 10pt Times Roman by BPCC Northern Printers Ltd, Stanley Road, Blackpool, Lancashire FY1 4QN; and printed by Hobbs the Printers of Southampton.

ISBN 0-85012-499-9

Acknowledgements

I would like to thank all the individuals and organisations who assisted in the preparation of this book. In particular I am indebted to British Telecom National Networks – PSS Marketing and British Telecom International – IPSS Marketing, for providing assistance and for reviewing the initial draft. We are also grateful to British Telecom for permission to use some of their diagrams (Figures 5.1, 6.1, 6.2, 6.3, 6.4, 6.5, 9.1).

The collaboration of the following organisations is also acknowledged with grateful thanks:

Burmah Castrol
Burroughs
Camtec
Dynatech
Eurolex
Gandalf
Geisco
IBM
Intel International
IRS - Dialtech
Istel
Pergamon Infoline
SIA
Starkey Laboratories
Telecom Gold
Whessoe (WCTS)

The Centre acknowledges with thanks the support provided by the Electronics and Avionics Requirements Board (EARB) for the project from which this publication derives.

Contents

1 Introduction

With the advent of telecommunications in data processing during the 1950s, computer communication designers were required to adapt the existing pervasive analogue telephony system to accommodate data transmission requirements. Today these facilities continue to be widely available and used. However, the accelerating growth of data transmission and the advent of digital switching and transmission technology, together with a desire by the PTTs to achieve maximum utilisation and efficient use of resources, led to the development in the late 1960s and early 1970s of public networks designed more specifically for the carriage of data.

Up to that time, apart from telex or telegraphy the data communications user had a choice between using the public switched telephone network (PSTN), or leased private circuits. Neither of these alternatives was completely suited to the requirements of data transmission.

Some of the limitations of the PSTN stem from the fact that being designed for speech transmission, constraints are imposed on the transmission of data. These include long call connect times, high error rates and low speeds. Many users have attempted to overcome these limitations by employing leased circuits to build private networks. Improvement in performance is attainable with leased circuits but usually at increased sophistication and cost.

Nevertheless the world's telephone networks have been adapted over the years to carry digital data traffic. Today the overwhelming advantages of digital transmission are encouraging the telecommunications administrations to convert from analogue to digital transmission.

During the late 1960s and early 1970s the PTTs began using digital techniques within sections of their telephone networks. Although this innovation had advantages for voice transmission, it was especially suited for data.

Packet switching which originated in the defence, research and academic worlds came to the attention of the PTTs at a time when there was a demand for improved data transmission services and a need to modernise networks. Packet switching was adopted by a number of administrations as a technique for providing a switched data transmission service which offered a number of advantages over PSTN. These included improved reliability and circuit utilisation coupled with reduced transmission costs derived mainly from the sharing of line and switching plant.

In the UK the Post Office Telecomms was the first national Telecomms Administration to explore this technique and launched the Experimental Packet Switched (EPSS) service in 1977. Following the success of this experiment the decision was taken to launch a fully operational public data service in 1981.

The adoption of Recommendation X.25 by the CCITT in 1976 as a connection standard for public packet switched netwo˙ ˙ provided a major impetus for expansion worldwide. As a result, most developed countries today have introduced public packet switched services. In parallel with these developments most countries, as in the UK, are proceeding with the modernisation of the public network with a migration to digital transmission.

At its inception, packet switching was as novel for the PTTs as for the prospective user. Apart from the realisation that it offered a range of new facilities over existing services and also provided opportunities for different tariffing principles to be adopted, there was hardly any commercial or business experience. Without doubt the PTTs had views based on their studies of the role and marketplace for packet switching services which were reflected in the shape of the tariff structure. However, the final test lay with the users' perception of the service.

The book *Why Packet Switching* (NCC, 1979) which derives from the NCC's participation in EPSS was published at the time of the launch of the public data service (PSS) in the UK. At that time only limited information about the service was available; most of the experience related to the experimental applications and other work mainly confined to the academic and research communities and special interest groups.

Now eight years on, PSS (Packet SwitchStream) has 'come of age'. Following the introduction of the UK X.25 service, manufacturers have gradually accepted the X.25 standard and produced increasingly efficient and cost-effective products; at the same time, major users have first experimented with, and then committed themselves to, packet switching.

BT no longer sees PSS as a complex operational service but as a network commodity with a proven record, extensive manufacturer's support and substantial operational experience. Of particular significance is BT's commitment to packet switching as a major 'open systems' service complementing the advances in the digital circuit switching and digital private circuits that are becoming more and more visible today.

This compares with the role previously adopted under the monopoly era in which BT, as a provider of a public service to all sectors of the community, primarily saw itself as educator. Today the situation is changing with liberalisation and the consequential introduction of competitive services, wider availability and enhancement of the PSS service, and BT's adoption of a more active policy of promotion.

Now PSS is reaching maturity, there is increasing opportunity for organisations to benefit from a communications service which is after all specifically 'designed for data'; however, before this can happen it is necessary to ensure that as wide a cross-section of industry and commerce as possible appreciates the role of public packet switching networks in relation to their specific communications needs. Accepting that the initiative for the marketing of the service must come from BT, the missing ingredient is guidance based upon the experience of others which welds the public service and existing and new communications services together to meet specific user needs.

With this in mind, the book has the following aims:

— to provide an update on *Why Packet Switching*;

— to develop further the role of packet switching and in particular PSS;

— to give as up-to-date account as possible on the PSS service and future developments in the service;

— to present guidance on the use of PSS by examining many of the applications to date;

— to consider the opportunities for the future.

In a sense, this book picks up where *Why Packet Switching* finished by building on the ideas and information of that time and enhancing these with the experiences over the first four years of operation. Much of the book is concerned with updating the information given on the PSS service itself. Chapter 3 provides an up-to-date description of the inland service and Chapter 4 gives information on the International PSS (IPSS) service.

But today PSS is taking on a new look. Considerable investment in both additional capacity and enhanced facilities has been announced by BT; Chapter 3 includes a description of the expansion plans and Chapter 5 covers the enhancements announced at the time of writing. Chapter 6 adds a further dimension to these descriptions by outlining the developments in associated BT networks and gateway services.

Although every effort has been made to ensure that the information provided is correct and up-to-date it is important to recognise that the situation still remains extremely fluid, especially in the aftermath of liberalisation and privatisation. The reader who wishes to obtain an absolutely up-to-date view of the service, its tariffs and relationships to other new services is advised to contact BT at the address given in Appendix 2.

With a wide readership in mind the book will be of interest to a broad cross-section of computing and telecommunications professionals; it is also likely to be of interest to other professionals who are daily becoming more involved with the development of business telecommunications services. These include office managers, system designers and management services staff or in fact anyone responsible for the planning and operation of telecommunications services. Because many of these may be relative newcomers, and because packet switching still remains a complex modus operandi, no apology is made for providing an introduction to packet switching in the earlier chapters of the book.

Packet switching and the X.25 standard are synonymous in the world of public data networks; without X.25 there would be little future for both national and international networking. Although X.25 is complex in depth, a sufficient understanding is important to any prospective user of the PSS service – to allow a grasp of the 'jargon' and to enable the full benefits of packet switching to be realised. With this aim Chapter 7 provides a 'broad-brush' description of X.25.

But X.25 and packet switching do not stop at public data networks. There is substantial interest and activity worldwide in the planning and development of private data networks based upon such techniques. This book only touches upon such matters being primarily concerned with the public data network. Hence in Chapters 7 and 8, only brief details of X.25 products and networks are provided. On the other hand, in Chapter 9 considerable attention is given to the support of devices attached to the network via packet assembler/disassembler (PAD) devices because these still play a very significant part in both private and public packet switched networks.

PSS is still a radically new category of service, a situation which has changed little since its birth. What *has* changed is the gaining of operational experience by both BT and users of the service. This has resulted in a clearer definition of its role. This is reviewed in Chapter 10.

To show how this role is reflected in market needs, the remaining chapters of the book are devoted to case studies selected as reasonably representative of the range of applications encountered at the time of writing. Each illustrates the strengths (and weaknesses) of the service in the light of specific user needs and draws out practical comment on individual experiences. Such experiences are summarised in the final chapter to provide a basis for the conclusions to the book and guidelines for prospective users.

The appendices are mainly self-explanatory but Appendices 7 and 8 warrant some comment. In Chapter 7 reference is made to host computer support of X.25 but as explained earlier, because of the nature of the topic covered by this book, only brief mention is made to the types of products offered by the major computer manufacturers and other software suppliers. To provide the reader with some further insight into this important sector of the market, Appendix 7 contains a description of X.25 support in IBM products. IBM was chosen because of the predominance of IBM systems encountered during the research for the book and hence referred to in the case studies described in the final chapters.

At the time of researching material, the VIIIth CCITT Plenary Assembly met to approve the proposed new and modified CCITT Recommendations. Due to the inevitable lag in publication of the 1984 Recommendations (Red Books), it was not possible to incorporate these in the main body of the book which is written around the 1980 Recommendations.

However, for the sake of completeness the changes made to the X.25
Recommendations are summarised in Appendix 8.

2 Packet Switching in Public Data Networks

THE EMERGENCE OF PACKET SWITCHING AND X.25

The packet switching concept was first proposed in the early 1960s for military communication systems, mainly to handle speech. It was proposed that speech should be digitised and transmitted in short bursts (packets) using a mesh type of network. It was subsequently realised that the technique with additional refinements might be ideally suited to the requirements of remote access computing systems. From the mid-1960s the technique was widely explored, initially almost entirely in the academic and research communities.

The chief benefits of packet switching were seen as follows:

— the subdivision of information into individually addressed packets in conjunction with alternative routeing arrangements enabled the transmission path to be altered in the event of congestion or individual link failure;

— the employment of additional intelligence within the network enabled more sophisticated error control and link control procedures to be applied;

— packets associated with different users or calls are clearly distinguishable and this provided the basis for an efficient form of statistical multiplexing, making variable speed transmission available to users according to the demands of their applications. With the incorporation of a suitable *flow control* mechanism, it also enabled speed and information handling disparities of communicating devices to be more closely matched;

— by employing wide bandwidth circuits for the trunk network,

21

substantial economies through extensive sharing of capacity could be achieved.

Apart from any other advantages, packet switching was seen as providing a relatively low-cost means of improving the reliability of analogue transmission networks.

From the late 1960s onwards, the UK Post Office, in common with other national administrations and common carriers, began to consider the long-term network modernisation requirements.

Several PTTs started to explore the possibilities of packet switching, the UK PO being amongst the first to establish an experimental network. At the time, this offered a low-cost alternative to PSTN, and could be grafted onto the analogue network without fundamental engineering changes.

The X.25 recommendation, which specifies the interface between packet-mode data terminal equipment (DTE) and data circuit terminating equipment (DCE) and which was approved by the CCITT in 1976, played a vital role in this development.

In November 1980, the CCITT plenary assembly approved the current version of the interface referred to as the 'CCITT Yellow Book'. Following its adoption by CCITT as a recommended class of service for public data networks, most of the major countries have established or are planning public packet switched networks, which are also being progressively interconnected internationally.

This chapter is intended to set packet switching in the context of public data networks.

PACKET SWITCHED DATA NETWORKS

Figure 2.1 illustrates a packet switched network and a typical packet format. A subscriber's equipment, whether a computer or simple terminal, is connected to the local packet switching exchange (PSE) which in its simplest form comprises one or more minicomputers. The PSEs are linked together by high-speed circuits to form the packet switching trunk network.

Data is formatted into packets of fixed maximum length. The packet header contains addressing information and various control fields. To ensure that packets are not corrupted during passage through the net-

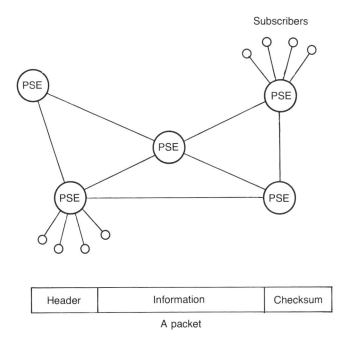

Figure 2.1   A Hypothetical Packet Switched Network

work, resulting in their loss or mis-delivery, 'sum-checks' are computed before a packet is transmitted and included, usually as a 'trailer' to the transmitted packet. Sum-checks are verified on reception at each exchange and, if found to be error-free, the packet is accepted and an 'acknowledgement packet' is returned to the sending exchange. Only when an acknowledgement has been correctly received, will the sending exchange delete the packet from its memory. If an error is detected, the exchange will retransmit the packet concerned. This mechanism provides a high degree of error-free data transfer between subscribers.

Because of the limited amount of storage provided at the switches, it is necessary to prevent excessive congestion. This is provided by a 'flow control' mechanism which enables PSEs where traffic is entering the network, to slow down or stop the sending of packets – either when there is a build-up at the switches, or where they are to be delivered to a device which operates more slowly than the sender. This provides the ability of the network to compensate for disparities in speeds of communicating devices.

Because the packets contain the source and destination address, they are transferred across the network as physical and logically independent entities. A consequence is that packets being exchanged between a number of users can be interleaved, and as much of the network resources are available to them as they can use.

This capability for load sharing derives from the type of multiplexing which is employed. This is a form of statistical or dynamic multiplexing which apportions the total bandwidth amongst users according to their demands. Because the multiplexing extends to the user's interface to the network, this also enables a large number of remote devices to be linked to a computer over one local access circuit, thus simplifying local connection arrangements.

A packet switched network may also provide adaptive routeing so that if the selected route is no longer practicable, either because of congestion or because of the failure of a link or a switch, then an alternative route will be determined if there is one available.

DATAGRAMS AND VIRTUAL CIRCUITS

Datagrams

The transport mechanism described above permits two users to send and receive data in the form of streams of individual packets. This is generally referred to as the datagram mode of operation. Although for certain categories of application this does have certain advantages, it also suffers from two major limitations. The first arises in practice because there may be a necessary logical relationship between packets. Hence it is vital that packets be delivered to an application program in the same sequence as they were despatched by the originator. Secondly, it would be clearly desirable for a computer to be able to engage in more than one conversation at the same time. For example, a number of remote terminals could be accessing different applications in the same host computer and, conversely, a number of sources could be sending messages to a single terminal.

The traditional solution to this second requirement using leased private circuits has been to place the responsibility for handling multiple calls and for exercising flow control with the centralised mainframe. However in a public switched network employing conventional circuit switching, multiple calls can only be established as a series of individual calls which must be co-ordinated outside the network.

These requirements can be met within a packet switched network, providing that there is a means of distinguishing between different calls. A mechanism is also needed for ensuring that the packet sequence is preserved. These facilities are provided by the 'virtual circuit' mode of operation.

Virtual Circuits

In packet switching networks where the notion of individual liaisons, or calls, is directly controlled by the exchange, the network is said to provide 'virtual circuits'. Packets passing between a subscriber and the exchange do not carry the two subscribers' addresses in the header as with datagrams but instead bear a reference number in the header indicating to which call they belong. In X.25 the reference number is called the 'logical channel number', the packet stream between the subscriber and the exchange being regarded as comprising a number of separate logical channels. The packet switching network can then make a logical association between one of the logical channels of one subscriber and a logical channel belonging to another. Figure 2.2 illustrates the concept

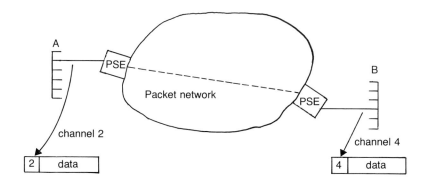

Figure 2.2   Virtual Circuit Operation

of the virtual circuit operation; and Figure 2.3 outlines the procedures involved in establishing and clearing down a virtual call.

In X.25 this is achieved in the following way. Each subscriber has a unique address (his line to the local exchange). This line is divided into logical channels, as described above. The calling subscriber chooses a 'free' logical channel from his available range of channel numbers, and sends a special packet called a 'call request' packet to the exchange.

This packet bears the chosen logical channel number in the header, but in the text body is placed the address of the called party. The local

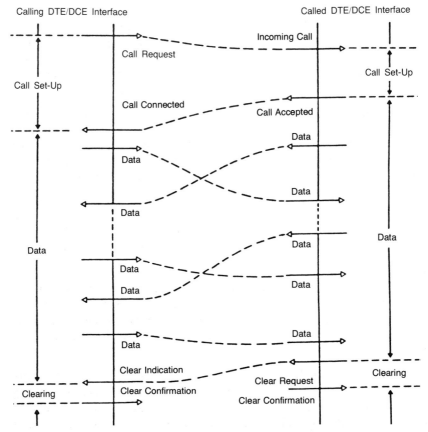

Figure 2.3   Call Establishment, Data, and Call Clear Phases of a Virtual Call

exchange makes a note of the channel number which the caller is using for this call, and then sends a 'call request' packet across the network to the exchange where the called subscriber is attached. The exchange at the called end chooses a free logical channel number from the range available to the called subscriber and transmits an 'incoming call' packet to that subscriber. This packet bears in the header the channel number chosen by the latter exchange and the address of the calling subscriber is put in the text body.

If the called subscriber can entertain the call, he will reply to his local exchange with a 'call accepted' packet, which is a very short packet bearing in the header the same channel number as chosen by the local exchange. The exchange will then send back a 'call accepted' packet across the network to the exchange at the originating end, which will forward it as a 'call connected' packet to the caller. Again this packet is very short and contains in the header the logical channel number originally chosen by the caller and noted by the exchange.

During this call establishment phase a user can request various optional facilities such as: reverse charging; high priority transmission; renegotiation of the flow control parameters. A particularly useful feature is the ability to cause further direction of the call, within the user's terminal equipment, by the use of a sub-addressing or process numbering field.

A virtual circuit now exists between the two subscribers, each of which knows it by the logical channel number at his end. Packets comprising the conversation or 'data phase' of the call can now be transmitted by either party. These packets will bear only the logical channel number as described above for the virtual circuit.

Either party may terminate the call by sending to the network a 'call clear request' packet bearing the logical channel number of the call at his end. The network will deliver a 'call clear indication' packet to the other party on his appropriate logical channel and erase the entries in the internal call control tables.

Compared with the datagram mode the virtual circuit mode offers several advantages. In addition to the preservation of packet sequencing across the network, the virtual circuit mode provides the capability to control data flow selectively on individual user sessions. For example, if congestion builds up on some region of the network only the virtual calls traversing that region are flow-controlled; the remaining circuits are left undisturbed. This contrasts with the datagram approach where local congestion tends to spread to the entire network before it can be halted.

After the virtual circuit has been established the end-to-end packet delay also tends to be lower. Delay fluctuations are less significant as the probability of network congestion is considerably reduced by strict control on new packet acceptance and path selection. In addition, if the user's average input rates and bandwidth requirements are known in advance, network bandwidth can be efficiently allocated at call-set up time. This form of bandwidth control coupled with route selection precludes the possibility of over subscribed trunks and buffer congestion.

Permanent Virtual Circuit

The virtual circuit corresponding to a 'virtual' call is a switched connection and the association only lasts for the duration of the call.

If the association is permanent, it is rather like a leased line running directly from one subscriber to another. Packets bearing the appropriate logical channel number as transmitted by the sender are routed by the network directly to the receiver, where they are delivered bearing the logical channel number appropriate at that end. This facility is called a permanent virtual circuit and is controlled by 'call tables' in the exchanges.

In addition to providing the basic mechanism for handling concurrent permanent and switched virtual circuits, Recommendation X.25 describes the procedures to be used between DTEs and DCEs for error control, maintenance of packet sequence on virtual calls, and flow control. These are described in more detail in Chapter 7.

SIMPLE TERMINALS AND THE 'PAD'

Within the context of X.25 as currently defined, the procedure for physically connecting to the subscribers serving PSE is determined by two main considerations: the amount of intelligence present in the device to be connected, and the characteristics (such as speed, synchronous/asynchronous transmission) of the access circuits.

For a full X.25 connection which supplies the logical channel multiprocessing capability and all the other features, the terminal must have enough intelligence to support the X.25 procotol. The user classes of service defined for X.25 also specify that access should be by dedicated circuits which operate synchronously, are fully duplex, and in a speed range which extends from 2,400 bits/s to 48,000 bits/s.

When X.25 was being defined it was recognised that there was a large class of simple terminals ranging from hard copy teletypes to teletype-compatible VDUs possessing only limited intelligence which was insuffi-cient to support X.25. In order to accommodate this category of terminal, the Packet Assembly/Disassembly (PAD) function was introduced. This is located in a PSE and its purpose is to implement the full X.25 protocol on behalf of a subscriber. It accepts serial strings of characters originated by an asynchronous (start/stop mode) character terminal, searches the character string for predefined 'packet delimiter' characters, and assem-bles the intervening characters into packets, the packets then being despatched across the network in accordance with the full X.25 protocol.

Similarly packets which are destined for a terminal connected to the PAD are converted into character strings by the PAD before being delivered to the receiving terminal. Figure 2.4 illustrates the function of the PAD.

CCITT Recommendation X.25 describes the interface for 'packet-

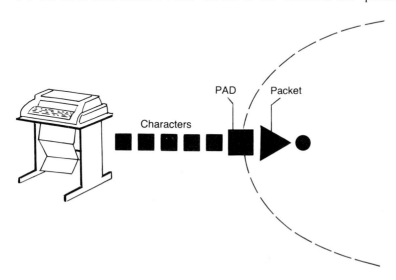

Figure 2.4   Function of the PAD

mode' DTEs. Three other specific CCITT recommendations – X.3, X.28 and X.29 – define communication between the start/stop (asynchronous) DTE and an X.25 DTE, as shown in Figure 2.5. X.28 defines how the start/stop terminal communicates with the PAD; X.29 defines how the X.25 DTE uses X.25 qualified data packets to control the PAD; and X.3 defines the operation of the PAD.

These recommendations effectively form an extension to X.25 for those hosts wishing to entertain access from such terminals, since an end-to-end dialogue must take place between the PAD and the host to facilitate control of a terminal. The implementation of these recommendations is discussed in greater detail in Chapter 9.

Access to PAD can be either by dedicated circuits or by dial-up over the public telephone network. The electrical connection to the access circuits is provided either by a Network Termination Unit (NTU) or a modem. The NTU implements CCITT Recommendation X.21 which is the electrical interface standard governing the connection of equipment to digital transmission circuits. The NTU is functionally simpler than a

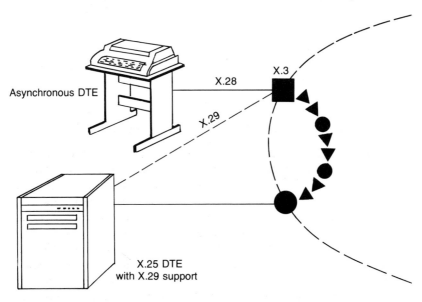

Figure 2.5   Communications between a Start/Stop DTE and an X.25 DTE

modem because with digital transmission there is no modulation/ demodulation requirement. Because of the large existing population of terminals designed to the V.24 specification, a transitional version of X.21 (X.21 bis) has been defined to enable these terminals to be accommodated.

The two modes of connection referred to earlier are described as the packet mode and the character mode, the description also being applied to the devices which are connected. Thus, the X.25 or packet mode will be the obvious form of connection requiring fast and accurate transmission, whereas the character mode would be employed in less demanding situations. These are the connection possibilities currently provided for by X.25.

The line speeds specified are those traditionally used for asynchronous start/stop character terminals: typically 110 and 300 bps. However, although these speeds were satisfactory for simple hard-copy teletypewriters, for applications involving screen-based terminals they are often too slow. Because of the growing popularity of such applications, today the 1200/75 bps and 1200 bps duplex services have become available in public data networks.

Some packet switched data networks have implemented PADs for which there are no CCITT recommendations. For example, several networks attach binary synchronous communication (BSC) devices to PADs for communication with X.25 DTEs.

OTHER RELATED X-SERIES RECOMMENDATIONS

In addition to CCITT Recommendations X.3, X.28 and X.29, usually refered to as 'The Triple X' recommendations, other recommendations used by public packet switched networks in conjunction with X.25 are X.1, X.2, X.75, X.96 and X.121. All these are summarised in Table 2.1. International connections can be made through two or more national public packet switched networks that are interconnected using X.75 as shown in Figure 2.6. Recommendation X.75 defines the CCITT interface for interconnecting public packet switched data networks. Based on Recommendation X.25, Recommendation X.75 defines interconnection for virtual calls (only), allows X.25 user facilities to span networks, includes internetwork accounting procedures, and provides certain technical enhancements, such as multiple links, between networks.

Recommendation X.1 defines start/stop, synchronous, and packet terminal classes of service for public data networks. Recommended data signalling rates, start/stop code structures and call control signals are given in X.1. Recommendation X.2 defines international user services

X.1	International user classes of service in public data networks
X.2	International user services and facilities in public data networks
X.3	Packet assembly/disassembly facility (PAD) in a public data network
X.21	Interface between DTE and DCE for synchronous operation on public data networks
X.21 bis	Use on public data networks of DTE which is designated for interfacing to synchronous V-series modems
X.28	DTE/DCE interface for a start/stop mode DTE accessing the PAD facility in a public data network situated in the same country
X.29	Procedures for the exchange of control information and user data between a PAD facility and a packet mode DTE or another PAD
X.75	Terminal and transit call control procedures and data transfer system on international circuits between packet switched data networks
X.96	Call progress signals in public data networks
X.121	International numbering plan for public data networks

Table 2.1   CCITT Yellow Book Recommendations (Volume VIII, VIIth Plenary Assembly, November 1980)

and facilities in public data networks; namely, for circuit switched services, leased circuit services and packet switched services. With respect to packet switching, X.2 defines X.25 and PAD services and facilities that are essential for all public packet switched data networks to implement. Recommendation X.2 also describes services and facilities that networks can additionally implement, and those whose classification is for further study in the CCITT.

Call progress signals in public circuit switched and packet switched data networks are used to inform the caller about the progress of his call.

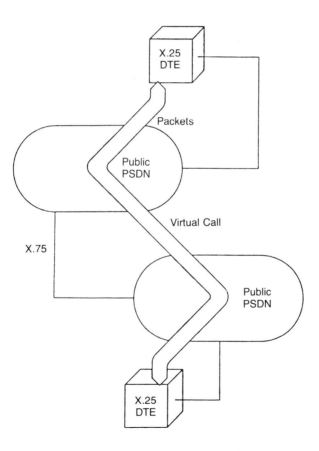

Figure 2.6   Network Interconnection using X.75

Types of call progress signals and whether a type is mandatory are defined in Recommendation X.96. Some call progress signals indicate circumstances that prevent connection with a called number; other signals indicate progress made towards establishing the call.

The international numbering plans and procedures for public data networks are given in Recommendation X.121 to facilitate interworking on a worldwide basis. Code formats for identifying countries, public networks inside countries, and network terminal numbers of data terminals attached to a given network are specified in X.121. The Director of the CCITT assigns country codes. It is a country responsibility to coordinate assignment of network codes inside the country.

3 The Packet SwitchStream (PSS) Service

INTRODUCTION

Packet SwitchStream (PSS) was introduced in the UK in 1981 and is now one of the many well-established data communication systems currently on offer from British Telecom. Since its launch, the number of subscribers has shown a steady increase and this has been accompanied by a progressive expansion of both the domestic network and arrangements for accessing national packet switched networks in other countries.

PSS is a national, public network designed and equipped specifically for the transfer of data by computers and terminals throughout Britain and with connections to networks in many overseas countries. It aims to complement, rather than supersede, other British Telecom data transmission services. PSS provides full-duplex working at a range of speeds up to and including 48,000 bits per second and it can also provide intercommunications between terminals which operate at different speeds.

Nationwide availability of PSS is assured by a special network. PSS exchanges are located in large towns and cities for convenience of installation. PSS has a distance-independent tariff, so new exchanges can be added to the network whenever growth demands, without the changes resulting in a revision of charges to individual customers, or any need for individual customers to review their arrangements.

The present network which has a hierarchical and modularised structure served approximately 4,000 customers at the end of 1984 and is doubling its X.25 port capacity each year.

All PSS switches are duplicated as a matter of security policy and have the protection of three levels of power supply. Network control and management is focused on Network Management Centres (NMCs) in London and Manchester. Each is a fully-duplicated computer system and is capable of running the complete network in an emergency.

PSS EXPANSION

Contracts of substantial value have been placed by British Telecom to strengthen the PSS network. The contracts announced in April 1984 provide for new packet switching exchanges to cater for growth in the number of customers and in the volume of calls within the United Kingdom and to other countries. At present, these are doubling each year.

BT expects growth to continue at a high rate as packet switching gets more users and its applications broaden into new value-added network services.

The network, which began commercial operation in 1981, consists of 100 switching units at 27 sites (as of September, 1985). Additional GTE/Telenet packet switches are being installed to extend the inland network; BT has placed further contracts with Plessey and introduced a second supplier BTM as part of its expansion programme.

There will be full intercommunication between the two kinds of switches. Figure 3.1 shows the growth, between 1981 and 1985, in the number of UK telephone subscribers having local-fee access to the PSS service.

A high-capacity switch has also been ordered by British Telecom International (BTI) for use in 1986 as a second international gateway to expand the international packet switched service (IPSS) described in Chapter 4.

At the time of writing, the existing GTE/Telenet gateway provided IPSS to 56 packet networks in more than 40 countries. This number continues to grow, and with it the volume of international packet data transfer.

In the Channel Islands, a co-operative venture – between the Jersey Telecoms and Guernsey Telecoms Board and BT – established a link to PSS during 1984. Connections are provided through BT Packet NetMux equipment installed at St Helier and St Peter Port. Customers are provided with dataline or dial-up access but not all PSS facilities.

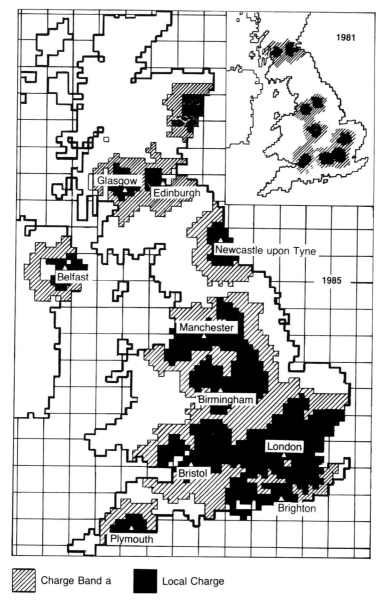

1981

1985

Glasgow
Edinburgh
Newcastle upon Tyne
Belfast
Manchester
Birmingham
London
Bristol
Brighton
Plymouth

▨ Charge Band a   ■ Local Charge

Figure 3.1   Growth in Local-Fee Access to PSS

Currently the PSS network uses the protocols which form part of the X series of recommendations for packet switching, adopted by the International Consultative Committee for Telephones and Telegraphs (CCITT) in 1980.

The network, and its new switches, will be subsequently updated to comply with more advanced protocols agreed by the CCITT in 1984.

BT's ultimate objective is to enhance the packet switched network so that it will fully support services complying with the emerging international standards for Open Systems Interconnection (OSI).

PSS IN-DEPTH

Introduction

PSS has been designed to conform as far as possible to international standards. In particular, the following CCITT Recommendations apply:

— X.25   Interface for Packet Mode Terminals

— X.3 ⎱ Procedures for handling of simple start/stop terminals
   X.28 ⎰ which require network Packet Assembley/Disassembly
   X.29 ⎰ (PAD) facilities

— X.75   Protocol for Internetwork Procedures

— X.121   Numbering Plan for Public Data Networks

These recommendations were outlined in the previous chapter (further information is given in Chapters 7, 8 and 9).

For a non-technical description of X.25 and the PSS protocol the reader should refer to the British Telecom booklet 'Packet SwitchStream – First steps in packet switching' (see Appendix 4).

All technical matters relating to the PSS protocol are contained in the British Telecom 'PSS Technical Users Guide' (see Appendix 4). This contains sections on all aspects of PSS including the non-technical areas such as literature, tariffs, facilities, and procedures for obtaining permission to connect.

Readers who require technical information about PSS should refer to the Technical Guide in preference to the documents referred to in this and other chapters which specify the X.25 and other related CCITT recommendations.

BT is committed to developing PSS to support OSI and to meet customers' needs and to support value-added network services (VANs). PSS already goes some way to supporting OSI through its adherence to international standards for the basic bearer service agreed in 1980. It will be developed to embrace further OSI standards adopted during 1984.

To ensure its full support for OSI, PSS is being enhanced (see Chapter 5), to support a wider range of access methods to match more closely the requirements of the broad spectrum of computers and terminals. Managed-network facilities and VANs which are added will be consistent with OSI standards where possible.

Customers' Equipment

All PSS customers have to provide their own terminal equipment. British Telecom does not recommend any models, nor does it designate approved suppliers.

All devices connected to PSS are referred to by BT as terminals in preference to the CCITT term Data Terminal Equipment (DTE). Terminals can be packet devices or character devices.

A packet terminal is one which complies with all three levels of the PSS protocol and can format and control packets and exchange packets with other terminals on the network. A character terminal is unable to comply with the 3-level protocol and requires the assistance of a PAD to communicate with other PSS terminals.

Before purchasing any equipment destined for use with PSS or any other British Telecom service the user should ensure that it is compatible with the speed, mode of working and facilities required, and that it has 'permission to connect' to PSS.

Permission to Connect

Permission to connect is generally sought by manufacturers who submit their new products to British Telecom. The equipment must have BABT approval to ensure that it cannot harm the functioning of the BT networks. In the case of intelligent devices, those parts of the software which affect the network, directly or indirectly, are examined by PSS. Once a particular product is a 'permissible attachment', individual machines do not have to be examined, with the exception that any software control of the British Telecom network is always examined at the time of provision of service. If the manufacturer has not applied for 'permission to connect', any company or even a private individual may do so.

By examining terminal equipment in this way it is not the intention of British Telecom to restrict the range of equipment available to customers, but to maintain a relevant grade of service for all users and to ensure the safety of those having any physical connection to the network.

BT is unable to proceed with the provision of access circuits until it is established that the terminal is a permissible attachment. The PSS Customer Services Group will then confirm 'permission to connect' with the equipment supplier.

Access Facilities

PSS supports a wide range of terminals, from teletypes to host computers. Access facilities are categorised by type of terminal (packet or character) and type of connection (dial-up or dataline).

A packet terminal is capable of constructing the package for transmission and reassembling the stream of incoming packets into messages. This type of terminal uses the CCITT X.25 protocol, which enables it to connect directly to PSS. Character terminals are simple devices, such as teletypes, which connect to PSS through a PAD (Packet Assembly/ Disassembly) unit. The PAD performs the tasks of packet assembly/ disassembly and call control.

Packet terminals are connected to the network by datalines – dedicated links to the packet switching exchange (PSE) – these are referred to as 'packet datalines'. Three line speeds are available: 2400, 9600 and 48,000 bits per second (bps). Datalines are also available to permanently connect character terminals to the PAD at the PSS exchange at 300 or 1200 bps. These are referred to as 'character datalines'.

Dial-up character terminal access is via the public switched telephone network to the PAD at either 300 bps, 1200/75 bps or 1200/1200 bps. The caller may use a modem (rented from BT or otherwise) or an acoustic coupler.

Packets and Calls

In PSS, 'octets' (8 bits) of data are assembled into packets, each packet normally consisting of a 'wrapper' of control information and up to 128 octets of user data. Longer packets can be requested by any user, up to a maximum of 1024 octets, by using the optional 'extended formats' facility (see later).

For charging purposes, each packet is counted using the unit called a 'segment'. This is 64 octets, or part thereof. For example a packet with 64 octets of user data counts as 1 segment, one with 65 octets as 2.

A number of packets transferred between two points form a call. PSS has two types of call – the datacall and the minicall.

The datacall is defined as having the three distinct phases referred to earlier: call set-up, data transfer, call clear. Call set-up involves the calling terminal sending an initial 'call request' packet to the distant terminal. If it is accepted, a 'call accept' packet is returned. The data transfer phase covers the flow of packets of user data, whilst 'call clear' is a final packet which terminates the datacall. Datacalls are available to 'packet dataline', 'character dataline' and 'dial-up' terminals.

The minicall is a short message (up to 128 octets) in the 'call request' packet. An equally short response may be included in the returned 'call clear' packet (see Minicall Send and Accept Facility description on page 55). Minicalls are available to 'packet dataline' and 'character dataline' terminals but 'character dataline' terminals can accept but not make minicalls. Dial-up 'character terminals' cannot make or accept minicalls.

Addressing

All terminals on PSS have a Network User Address (NUA). PSS will bill all charges to NUAs, and for this reason dial-up users are notified of the NUA which will be used by PSS for billing purposes.

All NUAs consist of 12 decimal digits as shown below, and two optional extra digits which are available for packet terminals only to use for sub-addressing.

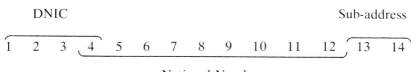

The first four digits of the NUA are known as the DNIC (Data Network Identification Code).

The first three digits of the DNIC identify the country, the fourth identifies the service within that country. The rest of the NUA from digits 5 to 12 identifies the particular dataline termination. In the UK the DNIC is 234 with a fourth digit '2' to identify PSS.

A packet terminal user must quote the full NUA of the number called, including the DNIC, whether calling a character terminal or another packet terminal.

A character terminal (dial-up or dataline) only needs to quote the 'national number' part of the NUA, digits 4 to 12, of the number called. This saves the trouble of entering the first 3 digits; the PAD will do this when it passes on the call request, but for international calls a prefix and full international number must be used.

Some packet terminals work as the gateway to a private network, or as a cluster controller for many smaller terminals. The terminals within their own network may be identified by means of the two 'sub-address' digits 13 and 14. PSS will carry these digits transparently (ie will be aware of their existence) but will neither change nor use them.

Call Information

Call information is provided automatically as a standard feature of the service for character mode terminals, and is available on a per-call basis for packet mode users.

This facility provides for details of the call duration and the number of segments received and sent to be shown at the end of the call, whether the call was originated by the terminal or not, and whether it was a chargeable or 'transfer charge' call.

Call information cannot be provided at the end of minicalls because the extra facility is incompatible with the minicall packet formats. Converted minicalls, which are terminated like a normal datacall, may show the call information.

DATALINE ACCESS FOR PACKET TERMINALS

Packet terminals access PSS through datalines that are permanently connected to PSS. The packet terminal is connected to PSS at power on and is automatically recognised as having PSS access rights.

Dataline Options

Three dataline options are available for packet terminals:

— Dataline 2400, giving a line speed of 2400 bits per second (bps) full duplex;

— Dataline 9600, giving a line speed of 9600 bps full duplex;

— Dataline 48K, giving a line speed of 48,000 bps full duplex.

All of these dataline facilities are for terminals operating synchronously in accordance with the CCITT X.25 protocol.

PSS Facilities

Packet terminals can make full use of the following range of facilities provided by PSS:

— Call redirection   (see Call Redirection Facility, p 52)

— Multiline   (see Multiline Facility, p 53)

— Closed user groups   (see Closed User Group Facility, p 53)

— Transfer charge
   acceptance   (see Transfer Charge Acceptance Facility, p 55)

— Minicall send
   and accept   (see Minicall Send and Accept Facility, p 55)

In addition to these facilities the packet terminal can exploit the following features of PSS:

— *Logical channels*. One physical link to the PSE is capable of carrying several logical channels of communications simultaneously. This means, for example, that a central computer does not have to poll all the attached terminals for input: the remote terminals simply call the host whenever they are ready. Logical channels can be designated as incoming only, outgoing only, or bothway; the channel allocation can be precisely tailored to user needs.

— *Packet retransmission*. A terminal can request the retransmission of a packet (or number of consecutive packets) for any reason.

Note that this is in addition to PSS requesting retransmission of any packets that are found to be in error.

— *Extended formats.* Extended format refers to certain packet formats which are longer than normal in two particular fields of the packet.

A subscriber to the extended format facility is thus able to transmit a 'call accept' packet in which the address field and facility field are both extended.

The ability to interpret extended formats is required in order:

(i) to accept minicalls (see Minicall Send and Accept Facility, p 55);

(ii) to be redirected to an alternative address when the address being called is out of order (see Call Redirection Facility, p 52);

(iii) to negotiate a change in packet size (see below);

(iv) to negotiate a change in window size (see below).

The extended format is not required by a subscriber who has been provided with the 'Call Redirection' facility but is required by a packet terminal user sending a call to such a subscriber at the time when his incoming calls are being redirected (see Call Redirection Facility, p 52).

Terminal equipments that are capable of operating with extended formats it is necessary to ensure that the software or facilities and features of PSS. To makes use of facilities requiring extended formats it is necessary to ensure that the software or terminal equipment is capable of handling the appropriate formats.

— *Packet size selection.* PSS normally carries information in packets containing up to 128 octets of user data. However, if terminal equipment is capable of handling extended formats it can negotiate a larger packet size (256, 512 or 1024 octets) with the terminal it is calling for datacalls on a per call basis. The packet size may be different for each direction of transmission, although the end-to-end size for calls in each direction must always be the same.

What Will It Cost?

The charges for dataline access for packet terminals are shown in Table 3.1.

Dataline Charges

Dataline	Once Only Connection Charge	Quarterly Rental
2400	£450	£437.50
9600	£800	£825
48K	Depends on distance to PSS	£2000

Facility Charges

Facility	Change of Facility Charge	Quarterly Charge
Call Redirection	£20	£5
Closed User Group	£20	£5
Dataline to alternative exchange	No charge	£625 (additional to standard charges)
Logical Channel	£20	£5
Minicall Acceptance	£20	No charge
Multiline	No extra charge	
Transfer charge acceptance	£20	No charge

Inland Call Charges (see notes on page 50)

	Volume charge per kilosegment			Duration charge per hour		
	Standard	Low	Cheap	Standard	Low	Cheap
Datacall	£0.25	£0.15	£0.15	£0.25	£0.15	£0.15

Table 3.1 Dataline Access Charges for Packet Terminals

Both parties involved in the call must have this negotiating capability, otherwise the standard value of 128 will apply. (This is known as the packet size default value.) The larger packet sizes may not be negotiated on minicalls.

All packet sizes are charged in the same way – ie per segment (or part) capable of containing 64 octets – so the same charge will be raised for a given number of segments whether they are carried in standard or larger-size packets.

— *Window size selection.* In order to prevent congestion, a mechanism is used to limit the number of packets the network can accept from any logical channel at a given time. The mechanism is known as a window. The size of the window refers to the number of transmitted packets, which may be from 1 to 7, for which acknowledgement is outstanding.

Equipment that cannot operate with extended formats is unable to negotiate window size and PSS imposes a fixed value of two (often referred to as the window size default value). It is only possible to negotiate window size for a datacall; it is not possible to negotiate window size for a minicall.

The effect of the window set at value two is that, at a given moment, some packets have arrived at their destination and have been acknowledged, two have entered the network and are in the process of being either sent or acknowledged, and some packets are waiting to cross the interface between the sender and the network. As soon as one of the two within the network has been acknowledged, another packet is able to enter it.

A window size of two is usually satisfactory for most users, but in certain circumstances a different size may be more appropriate.

DATALINE ACCESS FOR CHARACTER TERMINALS

Simple character terminals can gain access to PSS by a dataline. Dataline connection does not use the PSTN and the terminal is permanently connected to a Packet Assembly/Disassembly Unit (PAD). The terminal does not have to identify itself as it is automatically recognised by the PAD as having PSS access. Dataline connection allows simple devices, such as teletypes or other 'dumb' terminals, to use the wide range of facilities that PSS offers.

A dataline connection includes the modems at the user's site and at the PSS exchange, and a port at the PSE.

Dataline Options

Two dataline connections are available for character terminals:

— Dataline 300, giving line speeds of either 110 or 300 bits per second (bps) full duplex;

— Dataline 1200, giving a line speed of 1200 bps full duplex.

These dataline facilities operate asynchronously (the start/stop mode of transmission used by simple terminals).

PSS Facilities

A dataline character terminal can take advantage of the following PSS facilities:

— Closed User Group membership (see Closed User Group Facility, p 53);

— Transfer Charge Request and Acceptance (see Transfer Charge Acceptance Facility, p 55);

— Minicall accept (see Minicall Send and Accept Facility, p 55).

A character terminal cannot send minicalls and can only communicate with one destination at a time. Character terminals with dataline connection cannot have the call redirection facility, although calls from such a terminal may be redirected at the destination packet terminal.

Terminal Profile

The PAD holds a profile of the parameters used by the terminal to control certain functions during a call. Further information on PADs and PAD parameters is given in Chapter 9.

Calling Line Identification

Dataline character terminals are provided with the Calling Line Identification facility, for all incoming calls. The facility identifies the full NUA of the terminal that is originating the call. The Calling Line Identification is supplied, by the network, when the call is set up. Since the calling terminal is automatically identified by the network there is no need for the calling terminal to include its NUA in the message.

What Will It Cost?

The charges for dataline access for character terminals are shown in Table 3.2.

Dataline Charges		
Dataline	**Once Only Connection Charge**	**Quarterly Rental**
300	£200	£275
1200	£350	£275
Facility Charges		
Facility	**Change of Facility Charge**	**Quarterly Charge**
Closed User Group	£20	£5
Minicall Acceptance	£20	No charge
Transfer charge acceptance	£20	No charge

Call Charges (see notes on page 50)						
	Volume charge per kilosegment			**Duration charge per hour**		
Datacall	**Standard** £0.25	**Low** £0.15	**Cheap** £0.15	**Standard** £0.25	**Low** £0.15	**Cheap** £0.15

Table 3.2   Dataline Access Charges for Character Terminals

DIAL-UP ACCESS FOR CHARACTER TERMINALS

Character terminals may access PSS through dial-up connection to a Packet Assembly/Disassembly unit (PAD) at a PSS exchange. This enables simple devices such as teletypes or 'dumb' terminals to access the PSS, and use its wide range of facilities.

Dial-up access can operate as follows, using either a modem or an acoustic coupler:

— at a line speed of either 110 or 300 bits per second (bps);

— at a line speed of 1200/75 bps;

— at a line speed of 1200 bps duplex.

At all of these line speeds the service operates asynchronously (in the start/stop transmission mode used by simple terminals).

The dial-up connection is to the PAD at the PSE and once the call has been accepted the user controls the datacall through commands sent to the PAD (as described in Chapter 9).

The Network User Identity

In order to identify himself a PSS subscriber is issued with a special password known as a Network User Identity (NUI), which is recognised by the PAD. Access to PSS from a dial-up terminal cannot be gained without quoting the NUI and it is the user's responsibility to keep the NUI secure. The NUI consists of 12 alphanumeric characters of which the first six are chosen by the subscriber and the second six allotted by BT.

The NUI identifies the subscriber as being allowed access to PSS. It can be registered at more than one PAD so that the subscriber can always dial the local PAD, or dial a second PAD if the first is unavailable. A single NUI may also be used by a group of users with central billing requirements.

A single subscriber may have more than one NUI; each NUI being used for a separate purpose. Each NUI is subject to a separate charge.

Restrictions for Dial-up Access

A dial-up terminal must always be the initiator of a datacall. Dial-up terminals cannot receive incoming calls: though once the connection to the remote device has been made data can be passed between the two ends of the link.

PSS Facilities

A dial-up terminal can take advantage of the Closed User Group membership facility (see Closed User Group Facility p 53) and initiate a transfer charge call request (see Transfer Charge Acceptance Facility, p 55).

Terminal Profile

The PAD holds a profile of the parameters used by the terminal to control certain functions during a call. These PAD parameters are set initially, but may be changed to meet the requirements of a particular call.

Further information on PADs and description of facilities and procedures for communication with character terminals is contained in Chapter 9.

What Will It Cost?

Charges (see Table 3.3) for use of a dial-up connection are based on the use of the NUI. Charges for use of the telephone network (line rental, PSTN duration and distance based call charges) appear on the telephone bill. Charges for use of PSS services (NUI rental, volume and duration based datacall charges, facility charges) appear on the PSS bill.

These charges exclude the cost of the dial-up modem at the user's site which may be purchased outright or rented from BT or other suppliers.

Call Charges (see notes)

The charges for dial-up access for character terminals are shown in Table 3.3.

Datacall Charges (in addition to standard telephone charges)						
Volume charge per kilosegment				Duration charge per hour		
	Standard	Low	Cheap	Standard	Low	Cheap
Datacall (Dial-up)	£0.25	£0.15	£0.15	£1.00	£0.90	£0.90
Facility Charges						
Facility	Change of Facility Charge			Quarterly Charge		
Closed User Group	£20			£5		

Table 3.3   Dial-up Access Charges for Character Terminals

The only charge made for dial-up access to PSS is for provision of the NUI. The charge is a once only connection charge of £25 plus a flat quarterly rate of £6.25 per PAD.

Line speeds that can be used are 300 bps, 1200/75 bps and 1200 bps duplex. Charges for access are identical at all of these speeds.

CHARGES AND BILLING

Rates Applicable to Call Charges

Standard rates apply 8 am to 6 pm, Monday to Friday.

Cheap rates apply at all other times, plus Christmas day and New Year's day.

Low rates apply 8 am to 6 pm, Monday to Friday when:

— volume is greater than 1500 kilosegments and

— duration is greater than 1000 hours in each billing quarter for each Network User Address.

Notes Applicable to Call Charges

Subject to minimum charges, calls are charged in steps of 1 segment (volume) and 2 seconds (duration).

No charge is made if a call is cleared due to the network. All other datacalls are charged at a minimum of 20 segments plus appropriate duration charge.

A minicall, whether successful or not, is charged on a volume only basis equivalent to 20 segments.

A converted minicall (see Minicall Send and Accept Facility, p 55) is charged at the cost of the minicall plus the charge for the datacall.

Note that rentals are charged in advance while datacalls are charged for in arrears.

VAT is charged on all bills.

The tariffs given in this chapter are taken from PSS literature dated September 1984.

Billing

A variety of billing options is available. Bills can be provided in summary form only, or with full or partial itemisation at monthly or quarterly
intervals.

The summary form is available on-line to all PSS users by datacalling
2342190100620 and quoting their billing reference number together
with the unique billing password. Both items are recorded on the PSS bill.

PSS FACILITIES

Call Redirection Facility

The PSS Call Redirection facility allows the user to specify a second
address to which his calls are redirected when his packet terminal is
off-line. For example, if the terminal is switched off or the dataline is
down, a call to that terminal is redirected to a second (previously defined)
terminal. The caller is informed that the call request has been redirected
and given the new destination address. At this stage the caller has the
option of clearing the call.

In order to have the Call Redirection facility the receiving terminal
must be a packet terminal. A redirected call can be redirected again
provided the first terminal has the extended formats capability. The
second terminal must also be a packet terminal and have the redirection
facility. A datacall will not be redirected more than twice.

For call redirection to take place the sending terminal must be either a
character terminal or a packet terminal with the extended formats capability. PSS uses the extended formats capability to inform the sender of
the ultimate destination of the call. If the calling packet terminal does not
have extended formats then the call is cleared.

If the sub-addressing capability of PSS described earlier is used then
the following options for redirected calls are available:

— sub-address field unchanged on redirection;

— sub-address field set to zero on redirection;

— new sub-address field set on redirection.

It should be noted that if the user is a member of a closed user group
then the usual CUG restrictions apply to the redirected call.

In a practical sense the Call Redirection facility provides an extra level of resilience. If the packet terminal is out of service calls still get through to a second terminal.

Call redirection is also used to switch calls between terminals. For example, with an electronic mail application, on leaving the office and switching off the terminal calls can be transferred to another manned terminal where they can be acted upon. Alternatively they can be redirected between sites; for example, if one site is open during office hours and the other is available 24 hours a day.

Call redirection is available on all packet terminals for a once only connection charge and flat rate, quarterly charge.

Multiline Facility

The Multiline facility is available only to packet terminals and allows the user to have several datalines with the same network user address (NUA).

Normally all the datalines follow the same physical route. Different routeing, for extra security, can be negotiated with BT and may incur an additional charge. The individual datalines of a Multiline do not have to operate at the same transmission speed, but must terminate at the same PSS exchange. The Multiline facility allows a user to:

— issue one NUA to terminal users who wish to access his service. This means that although there may be several lines, users only have to remember one NUA;

— ensure that all calls can get through, no matter how many terminals are calling the NUA;

— provide an extra level of resilience. If one line goes down, calls can still get through on other lines without the sender being aware of the failure;

— carry a large total of call traffic without having to increase the transmission speed of any line.

Each dataline of the Multiline is charged at the standard rate and there is no extra charge for the Multiline facility.

Closed User Group Facility

The Closed User Group (CUG) facility gives the user the added privacy and security normally associated with a private network.

A CUG has a number of members who may communicate freely with each other over PSS. CUG members may be physically located anywhere in the UK and the Channel Islands.

Normally, terminals that are not members of the CUG cannot access the group's services and the CUG members cannot access services that are outside the CUG. As this totally closed system could be too restrictive, PSS provides a number of options for the CUG member as follows:

(a) Calls only to and from other members of the CUG;

(b) As for option (a) plus calls to any other PSS user (BT call this outgoing access);

(c) As for option (a) plus calls from any other PSS user (BT call this incoming access);

(d) As for option (a) but able, selectively, to both send and receive datacalls outside the CUG.

Each member of a CUG can have a different access option.

Any PSS subscriber can belong to one or more CUGs, without impairing the security of any of the groups. Membership of a CUG is the responsibility of the CUG controller; the person who requests the provision of the facility.

All access to CUGs is controlled in the network. Only datacalls that contain the correct identifiers and CUG membership numbers are connected. If the user is also using the call redirection facility the redirection address must have compatible CUG arrangements.

Examples of the use of the CUG facility include:

— providing privacy and security at a level previously associated with private networks;

— ensuring that members only make datacalls within the CUG;

— keeping sections of a business separate. For example, the accounting service could have a CUG of its own.

PSS users are charged a connection charge and a flat rate quarterly rental for each CUG to which they belong.

Transfer Charge Acceptance Facility

Any packet terminal, or character terminal with a dataline connection, can opt to accept transfer charge calls. Normally the calling party is charged for the call.

For a transfer charge request to be accepted the called terminal must have the Transfer Charge Acceptance facility. The called terminal can then accept or reject requests to transfer the charges on a call-by-call basis.

Any terminal, including dial-up, can request a transfer charge call.

Transfer charging is not available internationally or to the Channel Islands.

If a terminal requests a transfer charge call and the request is refused then the call is cleared. The requesting terminal is then charged for the call attempt.

A dial-up terminal that makes a successful transfer charge request is still responsible for the charges for the telephone call; only the PSS portion of the call charge may be transferred.

The transfer charge acceptance facility allows a user to:

— centralise charges, for example, in the use of an on-line informa-tion enquiry system;

— provide free access to a service, thereby allowing the service to be charged for on a subscription basis.

The transfer charge acceptance facility is available for a once only connection charge.

Minicall Send and Accept Facility

The minicall is a short message in the Call Request packet. An equally short response may be included in the returned Call Clear packet. This is often a useful option for sending very short messages.

With a normal datacall the network requires two control packets to be sent before there is any exchange of data packets, that is the Call Request packet and the Call Accept packet. A further packet, the Clear Request packet, is sent at the end of a call. None of these carry data.

With a minicall, up to 128 octets of user data may be carried by the Call Request packet if the call is for a packet terminal and data may also be carried in one short response, the Call Clear packet. For calls to a character terminal up to 124 octets of user data may be carried by the Call Request packet.

Minicalls are available to 'packet dataline' terminals and 'character dataline' terminals but 'character dataline' terminals can only accept minicalls. 'Dial-up' character terminals cannot request or accept minicalls.

For packet terminals, if required a minicall may be converted into a datacall. In this case the called terminal returns a 'call accept' packet instead of a 'call clear' packet in response to a minicall request. Data packets may subsequently be sent and received in the usual way. This type of call is referred to as a 'converted minicall'.

PSS ACCESS FACILITIES

The PSS access facilities described in this chapter are summarised in Table 3.4.

FACILITY	TYPE OF ACCESS		
	PACKET DATALINE	CHARACTER DATALINE	CHARACTER DIAL-UP
Outgoing Calls	Available – no charge	Available – no charge	Available – no charge
Incoming Calls	Available – no charge	Available – no charge	n/a
Call Redirection	Available – extra charge	n/a	n/a
Transfer Charge Request	Available – no charge	Available – no charge	Available – no charge
Transfer Charge Acceptance	Available – extra charge	Available – extra charge	n/a
Closed User Group	Available – extra charge	Available – extra charge	Available – extra charge
Additional Logical Channels	Available – extra charge	n/a	n/a

continues

FACILITY	TYPE OF ACCESS		
	PACKET DATALINE	CHARACTER DATALINE	CHARACTER DIAL-UP
Packet/Window Size Selection	Available – no charge	n/a	n/a
Multiline	Available – no charge	n/a	n/a
Minicall Send	Available – no charge	n/a	n/a
Minicall Accept	Available – extra charge	Available – extra charge	n/a
Call Information	Available – no charge (not for minicalls)	Available – no charge	Available – no charge
Dataline to alternative exchange	Available – extra charge	n/a	n/a

n/a – not available

Table 3.4   PSS Access Facilities

SUMMARY OF KEY NETWORK FEATURES

As we have seen in the preceding paragraphs, PSS gives its users some powerful system features. Some of these which are summarised here are an inherent part of the network, and are available to all users, whilst others are optional facilities, as listed in the preceding table.

— Logical channels. Each call uses one logical channel over a dataline and across the network. A packet dataline user can operate multiple logical channels and hence handle large numbers of simultaneous calls. This greatly increases the efficiency and cost-effectiveness of dataline access.

— Addresses and identities. Each dataline has a 12-digit network user address (NUA), which is comparable to a telephone number. The NUA is used during call set up but the network continues to identify packets that it delivers throughout a call by reference to this. A further two digits are available for sub-addressing within a host system.

— Dial-up character terminals identify themselves to the network by keying a network user identity (NUI), which is effectively a private password permitting network access. This may be shared by a group of users, but always results in one bill.

— Closed User Groups. This chargeable facility restricts access to and from one or more terminals, either just to calls with other members of the Closed User Group, or in one of a number of other combinations.

— Multiline. This facility links together a number of packet datalines so that calls can be shared between them.

— Call Redirection. This chargeable facility allows the redirection of incoming calls between packet terminals.

— Transfer Charge Acceptance. This chargeable facility allows any dataline terminal to bear the PSS charges for an incoming call.

4 International Packet Switching Services (IPSS)

INTRODUCTION

IPSS is British Telecom's international data communications service. It is the international extension of the UK's national public data service PSS to countries and data networks throughout the world. In 1984, the IPSS gateway provided connections to 56 public packet switched networks in more than 40 countries which spanned over 90% of the developed world. A number of additional routes are planned for connection in the future.

Any terminal on PSS can have access to the packet switching services of many other countries. If PSS is used to make international datacalls then the user only pays the international charges listed below. He does not pay inland PSS charges in addition to the international charges. If dial-up access is used, the user is responsible for the telephone charge for the call to the exchange.

A list of those countries to whom access is possible, as at April 1985, and their relevant tariffs is given in Table 4.1.

International access is very similar to inland PSS access: the major difference is that the NUA of the remote service includes the Data Network Identification Code (DNIC) for the relevant country.

The following PSS facilities are not available internationally:

— closed user group;

— transfer charge calls;

— minicalls.

The facilties that are available to the remote terminal are dependent on the packet switch service available in that country.

COUNTRY	NETWORK	TARIFFS	
		Duration per minute	Volume per 10 segment
*Argentina	Arpac	10p	4p
Austria	*Datex-P Radio Austria	2.2p	1.2p
Australia	Austpac Midas	10p	4p
Belgium	DCS	2.2p	1.2p
Brazil	Interdata	10p	4p
Canada	Datapac Globedat Infoswitch	10p	3.5p
Denmark	Datapak	2.2p	1.2p
Finland	Datapak	2.2p	1.2p
France	Transpac	2.2p	1.2p
French Antilles	Drompac	10p	4p
Gabon	Gabopac	10p	4p
Germany (Fed Rep)	Datex-P	2.2	1.2p
Greece	Helpac	2.2p	1.2p
Hong Kong	Datapak Intelpac	10p	4p
Indonesia	SKDP	10p	4p
Irish Republic	Eirepak	2.2p	1.2p
Israel	Isranet	10p	4p
Italy	Itapac	2.2p	1.2p
Ivory Coast	Sytranpac	10p	4p
Japan	DDX-P Venus P	10p	4p
Luxembourg	Luxpac	2.2p	1.2p
*Malaysia	Maypac	10p	4p

continues

COUNTRY	NETWORK	TARIFFS	
		Duration per minute	Volume per 10 segment
*Mexico		10p	4p
Netherlands	Dabas Datanet 1	2.2p	1.2p
New Zealand	Pacnet	10p	4p
Norway	Datapak	2.2p	1.2p
Portugal	Telepac	2.2p	1.2p
*Reunion		10p	4p
Singapore	Telepac	10p	4p
South Africa	Saponet	10p	4p
Spain	Iberpac TIDA	2.2p	1.2p
Sweden	Datapak	2.2p	1.2p
Switzerland	Telepac	2.2p	1.2p
**USA	Autonet Compuserve ITT-UDTS RCA-LSDS Telenet TRT Datapak Tymnet Uninet WUI-DBS	10p	3.5p

Data calls to but not from the UK can also be made from

*Bahamas, Bahrain, Barbados, Bermuda, *Cayman Is, *Hungary, Oman, Philippines, Rep of Korea, United Arab Emirates, Taiwan, Thailand.

Once calls have been set up, data can flow in both directions.

NOTES   *Not yet connected to IPSS. The tariffs shown are those which are expected to apply on introduction of the service.

**Bulk Discounts – Any duration in excess of 500 hours and/or any volume over 500 kilosegments of data to the US from any one NUA in a normal billing quarter will be charged at 50% of the normal rate ie £3.00 per hour and/or £1.75 per kilosegment. This facility is currently offered on a trial basis.

Table 4.1   Accessible Countries

OTHER IPSS SERVICES

INMARSAT Maritime Satellite Service

Ships at sea and oil rigs can use IPSS data communication services via satellite links through the INMARSAT service connection to the IPSS gateway. Access is provided for dial-up connection from the vessel at 300 bps.

Tariffs for this service are those given earlier for the international connections plus an additional charge for the INMARSAT call to the UK.

Visitor Service

For visitors to the UK, BT offers an on-demand dial-up access facility to the IPSS gateway. Aimed at the UK business visitor the service provides immediate connection to IPSS. A subscriber to this service is issued with an IPSS Network User Identity (NUI) which allows dial-up access to the London based gateway service.

This service is nominally available for a period of 3 months at a charge of £25 for the initial connection and £5 for rental of the NUI. Line speeds of 300 bps and 1200/75 bps can be used.

FURTHER INFORMATION

Requests for further information on IPSS services and enquiries concerning particular networks, network directories, etc, should in the first instance be directed to BT International Data Services at the address given in Appendix 2.

A constantly updated list of countries and networks currently available or planned for early connection is also available to PSS users on the BT Hostess computer. Similar information is available to Prestel users on Prestel Page 38580927.

INTERNATIONAL TELETEX SERVICE

An International Teletex Service to be introduced progressively following the opening of the UK service, will develop on a country by country basis as international service agreements are negotiated. Access to this service will be provided by extending the UK service over IPSS.

For PSTN based Teletex terminals this will be via InterStream Two and PSS. For PSS based Teletex terminals it will be direct. UK Teletex users will gain access to International Telex via the InterStream Three service when it becomes available. Chapter 6 gives more information on the InterStream services.

5 MultiStream

INTRODUCTION

In accordance with BT's strategy of supporting Open Systems Interconnection Standards, PSS is to be enhanced to support a wider range of access methods.

Experience with PSS has shown that the X.25 network alone cannot meet all the cost/performance requirements of the user market place. A development called 'MultiStream', which was announced in outline in 1984, broadens the PSS service by providing widespread local coverage and a wide range of access protocols. The MultiStream node which is a development of the BT Packet NetMux is being installed physically close to major high streets, industrial estates and business centres throughout the country to bring the service closer to the customer and to make its use more cost effective by providing local call-fee dial-up access over a wider area.

MultiStream nodes will be installed at a significant rate – such that from an initial coverage of 58 sites in April 1985, the service will rapidly grow to over 1000 sites. The ultimate objective is to have such a node in every significant local telephone exchange.

Although PSS is based on the basic CCITT X-series Recommendations these interfaces are not considered sufficient for many networking requirements. The Triple-X interface is recognised as providing a simple, but unprotected, and rather unfriendly, character terminal access to the service. On the other hand, the X.25 interface provides a very comprehensive switching and multiplexing protocol which is ideal for supporting large host systems which utilise the inherent multiplexing feature, but is not always cost effective for smaller hosts or intelligent terminals.

These interfaces represent the extremes of a spectrum of access protocol requirements; MultiStream fills the middle ground by providing a range of protocols, some 'open' some 'proprietary' to match more closely the broader spectrum of computers and terminals.

As shown in Figure 5.1 these protocols include:

— a more friendly but still unprotected version of the CCITT PAD (called the 'CPAD');

— an error-protected asynchronous access protocol (called the 'EPAD');

— specialised Videotex support over PSS (called the 'VPAD');

— support for IBM 3270 (called the 'BPAD').

In addition to support for the full X.25 interface, MultiStream offers support for *one* and *four* virtual circuit X.25 subsets. These are seen as being particularly attractive to users of Teletex terminals and professional 'multi-window' microcomputers.

EPAD and VPAD services were launched in 1985 with the remaining services due in the following year. Tariffs are set to fill the spectrum between the existing Triple-X (character mode) terminal and the full X.25 (packet mode) terminal tariffs reflecting the functionality of the service. EPAD direct connection in a local exchange area will be significantly less than current PSS dataline charges. Dial-up facilities will now be available to a high proportion of users with local call-fee access.

MULTISTREAM EPAD

For asynchronous access EPAD provides error detection on the link between the network and the terminal, by means of EPAD software at both the exchange and customer installation (in either the modem or terminal).

Information from the user terminal is transmitted in blocks which are wrapped up by control characters. If the control characters are not correctly received the EPAD automatically requests the terminal to retransmit the block of information. Any errors are discarded and the user only sees the actual information. This access protocol will benefit users by providing end-to-end data security over the unprotected link between dial-up asynchronous terminals and the PSS PAD.

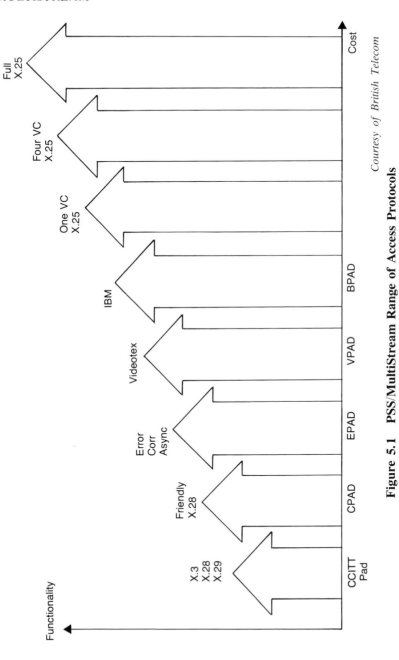

Courtesy of British Telecom

Figure 5.1   PSS/MultiStream Range of Access Protocols

MULTISTREAM VPAD

VPAD, dial-up videotex access, is designed to meet the needs of private viewdata system users. It will accept 'standard' viewdata terminals normally used for dial-up access with call set-up controlled by on-screen 'menus'.

VPAD is accessed via a desk top connection but once connected the user can log in and out of various hosts whilst still maintaining the telephone connection.

MULTISTREAM FACILITIES

It is worth highlighting the following MultiStream facilities:

— Dialling-up MultiStream

A MultiStream dial-up user will usually phone the nearest Multi-Stream exchange which provides the service required. A particular telephone number is related to a particular MultiStream service at the exchange.

— MultiStream Passwords

MultiStream passwords are the key to accessing the service. Dial-up customer's tariffs are based on a nationally available password which allows a single connection across the network. If customers or their users wish to make a number of simultaneous datacalls across MultiStream then they need to subscribe to multiple call passwords. Each simultaneous call incurs a further password fee.

A MultiStream customer is able to access the service and change his password using a simple on-line procedure. Each password is uniquely mapped against the customer's billable NUA (see below).

To change the password additional identity is required. This is the unique 'Administrator's password' which is selected by the customer who originally applied for service. These identities are also uniquely mapped against billable NUAs.

Normally one password per service purchased is selected but if preferred a customer can use the same password when accessing two or more MultiStream services. In this case the same billable NUA is applied to a number of services. At the other extreme, a customer can apply for a number of passwords for use on a particular MultiStream service such that various parties can be allocated to different passwords.

— User Message

Owners of MultiStream passwords can choose their own custom-ised headline banner page, up to 64 alphanumeric characters in length, which is displayed whenever the password is used to log-on to MultiStream. If desired a new banner page can be selected by the Administrator on-line.

— Billable NUAs

'Billable NUAs' are unique identities allocated by BT to Multi-Stream customers and normally each customer will be given one billable NUA per MultiStream service purchased.

The billable NUA is the identity against which MultiStream customers are billed and is the identity requested for maintenance services.

— Calling Line Identity

Every owner of a MultiStream password is allocated a 'Calling Line Identity' (CLI). The CLI which identifies a caller using MultiStream consists of 14 characters comprising the PSS 'Data Network Identification Code' (DNIC) described in Chapter 3, followed by the 'billable NUA', followed by 00.

       DNIC   Billable NUA
   ⎴   ⎴
   2 3 4 2   n n n n n n n n   0 0

— Host Addresses

As described in Chapter 3, all terminals on PSS have a Network User Address (NUA) which is made up of 12 decimal digits with a sub-address of 2 extra digits. Three options are available to MultiStream customers in specifying the address to which a datacall is made – auto call, menu selection, and open network.

Auto Call gives immediate access to one particular address by automatically establishing the appropriate connection. Menu Selection presents a menu of a small number of different addresses from which the user can select the appropriate entry. Open Network allows datacalls to any address linked to PSS by keying in the appropriate identity.

A further option allows MultiStream customers to substitute a mnemonic of up to 8 alphanumeric characters in length for short code Menu Selection.

— Parameters

MultiStream customers are able to select a range of CCITT X.3 parameters for defining the appropriate PAD characteristics and non-standard parameters which have been implemented to cater for extended features.

The parameters which are affected by the EPAD are as follows:–

    Parameter 1   – Escape from data transfer
    Parameter 2   – Echo control
    Parameter 6   – Suppression of service signals
    Parameter 7   – Action on receipt of break
    Parameter 8   – Suppression of data
    Parameter 21 – Block check

As an alternative to selection of individual parameters, six standard EPAD parameter profiles (P0 to P5) are provided; profile P0 is used unless others are specified by the customer.

The parameters which are affected by the VPAD are as follows:

    Parameter 2 – Echo control
    Parameter 4 – Time-out value

Once selected the chosen parameters are mapped against each customer's unique MultiStream password.

— Security

BT keeps no record of the MultiStream or Administrator passwords selected. Administrators are able to change their MultiStream passwords as often as they need in order to meet security requirements and are free to issue passwords to any parties they might wish to use their MultiStream services.

WHAT WILL IT COST?

MultiStream Password Charges

The unit charge for a password is £25 per quarter. This allows one call across MultiStream; if several simultaneous calls are required then the charge will be the number of calls times the unit charge. If the same password is used for several protocols then a charge is made for each protocol.

MultiStream Charges for PSS Usage

A single rate is charged for both volume and duration regardless of the time of day.

MultiStream Service	Volume charge per kilosegment	Duration charge per hour
EPAD	£0.25	£0.25
VPAD	£0.25	£0.25

MultiStream calls are charged in steps of 1 segment (volume) and 1 second (duration).

VAT is charged on all bills.

The tariffs given above are taken from MultiStream literature dated April 1985.

Reverse Charges

If a PSS customer has subscribed to the Transfer Charge Acceptance facility (see Chapter 3) then a MultiStream customer can elect to reverse charge to that address. A reverse charge datacall is then levied against that PSS address.

6 The Evolving Services

INTRODUCTION

It is recognised by BT that one of the major disadvantages of the existing BT telecommunications infrastructure is that it is based on separate and largely independent networks. This situation imposes two major constraints on the user:

a) the need for dedicated access to each network for which use is required

b) the need for a range of identities (numbers) each of which must be disseminated to all existing and potential correspondents.

The consequences of this situation are increased costs and associated administrative inconvenience which add to overall business overheads. The existing arrangements are also often a limiting factor for many potential users of public telecommunications services because in general a relatively high usage rate is required to justify the cost of access to, say, the PSS network.

The ultimate objective is to establish a common, multi-service connection to an integrated network, ie a network capable of carrying all types of communication.

The Integrated Services Digital Network (ISDN) with its ability to provide enhanced intelligence in the network will permit a wide range of both voice and non-voice services to be supported. Advanced services, such as voice messaging and other Value Added Network Services (VANS), can be fully exploited to enhance the value of the network.

The first steps on this evolutionary path are already emerging. With ISDN the Integrated Digital Access (IDA) facilities offer access to both

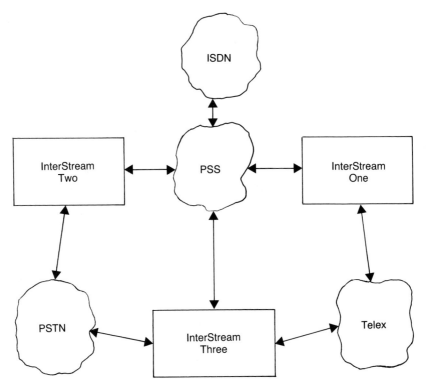

Courtesy of British Telecom

Figure 6.1   Teletex/Telex Conversion

PSS and the analogue PSTN; and 'gateways' (InterStream One, Two, and Three) provide interconnections between the PSTN, Telex and PSS networks (see Figure 6.1).

In the longer term, a switched 2 Mbits/s transmission is likely to emerge and this will form another element within the ISDN. Also a switched wideband capability, developed to meet the needs of the distribution of entertainment video, will be required and in due course this will be incorporated into the ISDN.

Eventually the various switching and transmission capabilities and associated services will merge to provide a fully integrated services digital network.

INTERSTREAM

InterStream is the BT nomenclature for a series of gateways, which for users of PSS extend their access to other BT services:

— InterStream One gives access to and from the Telex network;

— InterStream Two gives access to and from the PSTN;

— InterStream Three provides a Teletex-to-Telex Conversion Facility for users of Teletex terminals on both PSS and the PSTN.

InterStream One, the first of the PSS gateways, is available as a service to all UK Telex and PSS subscribers. The gateway which is a Telex Network Adaptor (TNA) handles all protocol conversion for each network, so that a Telex subscriber can communicate with PSS-based customers and other users.

In the UK, Teletex makes use of both the PSTN and PSS networks. InterStream Two allows messages to be sent between a Teletex terminal on the PSS to a Teletex terminal on the PSTN. The InterStream Two gateway which is a Packet Network Adaptor (PNA) only provides Teletex message transfer between the PSTN and PSS.

InterStream Three is a store-and-forward facility specifically designed to allow the transfer of messages between the Teletex services, on either the PSTN or PSS, and the Telex network.

INTEGRATED SERVICES DIGITAL NETWORK (ISDN)

British Telecom is in the process of creating a multi-purpose Integrated Digital Network (IDN) based on System X exchanges, interlinked with digital transmission and common channel signalling. Extending this IDN by providing customers with digital access links will create an Integrated Services Digital Network (ISDN), capable of supporting a wide variety of both voice and non-voice services.

The Pilot ISDN

In order to give users an early introduction to ISDN and encourage its rapid exploitation, BT has introduced a Pilot ISDN service during 1985.

The intention is for the Pilot service to expand to become a national ISDN and all local exchanges will eventually have ISDN capabilities. The Pilot is not intended as an experiment or field trial.

Integrated Digital Access (see Figure 6.2)

Customers access the ISDN through local access facilities marketed as Integrated Digital Access (IDA), available in two basic forms: single-line IDA and multi-line IDA.

Single-line IDA provides the capability for two simultaneous connections to two independent destinations and comprises:

  − a connection of up to 64 Kbits/s for voice or non-voice use;

  − a connection of up to 8 Kbits/s for non-voice use.

In the customer's premises a Network Termination Equipment (NTE) provides standard CCITT interfaces to the customer's terminal equipment. Its functions include any protocol and rate adaption required,

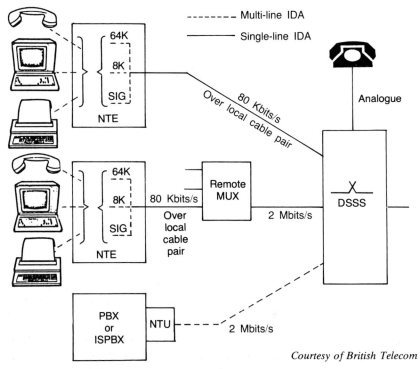

Courtesy of British Telecom

Figure 6.2   Integrated Digital Access (IDA)

multiplexing of the two access channels and an 8 Kbits/s signalling channel to an 80 Kbits/s aggregate, and termination of the full duplex digital transmission system which operates over a 2-wire local line to the exchange.

For the initial phase of ISDN service, two NTEs will be available. NTE1 includes a digital telephone, keypad, display, and a data port capable of operating at up to 64 Kbits/s using an X.21 bis interface or X.21 (leased line variant). NTE3 comprises a wall-mounted remote unit providing up to six data port connections selected from a range which includes:

— X.21 (leased line variant) and X.21 bis;

— X.21 (circuit switched variant);

— 2-wire analogue;

— V.24/V.28;

— MODEC.

The MODEC is a combined modem and codec, working at up to 300 bits/s which allows communication between low-speed RS232 terminals connected to IDA and similar terminals connected to the PSTN via modems.

The 2-wire analogue interface enables existing analogue equipment, including answering machines, modems and existing Prestel sets, to interwork between ISDN and PSTN.

To make single-line IDA available in non-ISDN exchange areas, BT will be providing out-of-area service. This will be provided by IDA multiplexers placed in non-ISDN exchanges and each providing up to 15 single-line IDAs.

Multi-line IDA has been developed for customers using a digital PBX. The term employed to describe such a PBX is an 'ISPBX' (an Integrated Services PBX). This gives a customer up to thirty traffic channels, with a dedicated channel for signalling. All these channels are carried on a single 2 Mbits/s PCM system.

In addition to the normal range of System X services there are two main, data-only supplementary services included in the initial phase of ISDN. These are: Closed User Group and Calling and Called Line

Identification. They are available to both single-line and multi-line customers.

Customer Services Available via IDA

ISDN will offer a digital path with common-channel message-based signalling from the NTE/ISPBX at the customer's premises to the network. This facility provides the customer with an integrated access to a wide range of voice and non-voice services. Some of these services are also supported by dedicated networks or the existing telephony network, while others are unique to the ISDN.

The Pilot ISDN will support the following bearer services:

— Circuit switched synchronous data (2.4, 4.8, 8, 9.6, 48 and 64 Kbits/s);

— Circuit switched asynchronous data at speeds up to 9.6 Kbits/s;

— Digital Private Circuit Data with rates from 2.4 to 64 Kbits/s;

— ISPBX access via a 2 Mbits/s digital path;

and it will provide access to the following Telecommunication Services:

— Prestel and photo videotex;

— Packet SwitchStream;

— Teletex;

— High-speed facsimile;

— Slow-scan TV;

— Telephony service.

Interworking ISDN to PSS

The ISDN will be introduced into an environment of developed networks. It is therefore necessary to interwork with these networks until such a time as they are absorbed by the ISDN, in order to permit access to and from their customers or facilities. This section describes methods of interworking between the ISDN and PSS.

Asynchronous Service

It will be possible for ISDN customers to access Packet SwitchStream

(PSS) from asynchronous terminals, via dial-up connections. Calls are set up to the originating PSE by dialling a PSE access number or alternatively by using an NTE-provided hot-line facility. Once the initial connection is complete, standard in-band protocols between the ISDN customer and the PSE-based Packet Assembler/Disassembler (PAD) identify the calling and called customers and PSS completes the connection.

Calls incoming to an ISDN customer cannot be supported, since the PSS-based PAD has no means of signalling destination address to the ISDN.

Customers may choose either analogue or digital interworking as follows:

— Analogue interworking

This method is shown in Figure 6.3. In order to interwork with PSS-based PADs, ISDN users must employ NTE interfaces which allow end-to-end compatibility with the PSE-based modems. This compatibility is achieved by use of an analogue port plus modem or, alternatively, a modec port. Both options are available on NTE3, the modec being restricted to a maximum of 300 bits/s whereas the modem option can interwork at any of the PSS dial-up rates (110, 300, 1200/75 or 1200 bits/s duplex. Both options require use of the 64 Kbits/s (B) channel.

ISDN customers access the same shared PAD plus modem combinations in PSS as analogue customers – no special PSS provision is required.

— Digital interworking

For digital interworking shared PAD/NTE combinations are provided in the place of shared PAD/modem combinations at the PSE, and are accessed across the ISDN using ISDN digital calls. The method relies on a digital path being available across the network to the PSE, but carries the advantage of eliminating the need for modems/modecs. V.24 interfaces are employed instead, allowing service from both NTE1 and NTE3. Either the 8 Kbits/s or 64 Kbits/s channel may be used on an NTE, but the data rate is restricted to the PSS PAD rates available (maximum 1200 bits/s duplex).

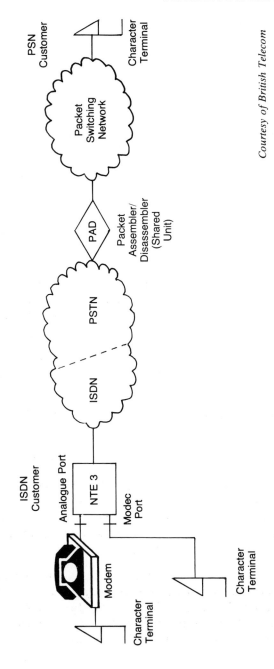

Courtesy of British Telecom

Figure 6.3   Asynchronous Packet Access – Analogue Interworking

This service, which involves installing NTE/PAD combinations at the PSE, will only be provided if there is sufficient customer demand.

Synchronous Service

The synchronous method of access more fully exploits the capabilities of the ISDN, offering higher speed access and eliminating the need for modems. As such, it should be cheaper than the existing 48 Kbits/s dataline service. Two options are available:

— Dial-up service via a Packet Network Adaptor (PNA)

This service (shown in Figure 6.4) utilises a number of dedicated ISDN ports being provided on a Packet Network Adaptor (PNA). This adaptor is being installed in the network as a PSS/PSTN gateway to cater mainly for Teletex traffic between the networks. This interworking arrangement is marketed as the InterStream Two service described earlier. The PNA is accessed across the ISDN using an ISDN digital call, and the set-up through PSS is then completed using X.25 set-up procedures in-band between the terminal and the PNA.

Either the 8 Kbits/s or 64 Kbits/s channel may be used on an NTE, but the user data rate chosen must be compatible with the PNA port.

Using this mode of access, a user will be charged ISDN and PSS call charges, plus a PNA charge.

— Dial-up/private circuit service via dedicated NTEs

For customers with high usage of PSS (eg ISPBX customers with one channel permanently connected into PSS), it will be advantageous to BT (in order to reduce loading on the PNA) and the user (to avoid PNA charges) to produce an alternative access arrangement to using the PNA.

This service (shown in Figure 6.5) utilises an NTE at the PSE which is dedicated to each customer in order to provide point of entry information for charging purposes. Fraudulent use by other customers is barred either by leased line access or by utilising the Closed User Group facility on dial-up access.

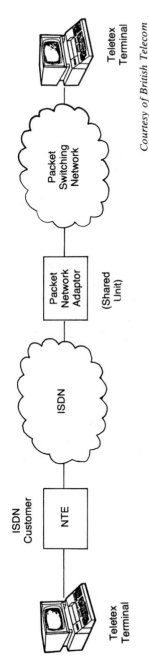

Courtesy of British Telecom

Figure 6.4   Synchronous Packet Access via a Packet Network Adaptor

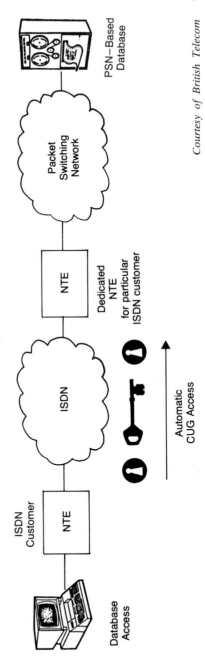

Courtesy of British Telecom

Figure 6.5   Synchronous Packet Access via Dedicated NTEs

All PSS data line rates, including 48 Kbits/s, will be available by this method.

Teletex

As mentioned earlier, the provision of ISDN access facilities to PSS and PSTN, together with the InterStream gateways, will make it possible for terminals on ISDN, PSTN, Telex and PSS to communicate.

Teletex terminals will be supported in two ways with IDA: either via a modem, or via synchronous digital interfaces. Modem-based terminals will be capable of interworking with other PSTN or ISDN-based terminals using ordinary telephone calls without requiring interworking units. Interworking with PSS-based terminals will be provided via the Packet Network Adaptor (PNA) described earlier, accessed via the PSTN port. This interworking arrangement is marketed as the InterStream Two service referred to earlier. Interworking with Telex terminals is achieved via the Teletex Conversion Facility marketed as InterStream Three.

Two types of terminal will be supported in ISDN via synchronous digital interfaces: the X.21/X.25 terminal and the PSS Teletex terminal. The X.21/X.25 terminal may be connected to the full X.21 port of NTE3, or to the X.21 leased line port on both NTE1 and NTE3. The PSS-based Teletex terminal which employs the V.24 interface is supportable on both NTE1 and NTE3.

Full interworking between IDA terminals of these types will be available across the ISDN. Interworking with all other terminals will be via the InterStream Two accessed via the X.21 port. Subsequent interworking will embrace the InterStream Three gateway where the target terminal is in the Telex network.

7 More About X.25

INTRODUCTION

In the preceding chapters, considerable reference has been made to CCITT Recommendation X.25, both in the outline description of packet switching services and the fuller description of the PSS service. The 1980 revised recommendation itself contains over 90 pages and is not structured in a way which gives a ready grasp of what X.25 is. This chapter brings together the references made earlier to X.25 and provides, in broad-brush terms, a fuller explanation of X.25.

Recommendation X.25 defines the interface between data terminal equipment and the public network for terminals operating in the packet mode. It does not imply how the network functions internally, nor does the sequence of events at the interface imply precise information about what is happening at the corresponding interface between the network and the remote party. The only constraint on the network is that packets belonging to a virtual call are delivered in the same order as they are transmitted.

The recommendation is split into three sections which identify separately the main functional components of X.25, and which correspond to hierarchical levels in the design (Figure 7.1).

These are:

Level 1   the physical interconnection where the electrical signals pass between the Data Terminal Equipment (DTE) and the Data Circuit-terminating Equipment (DCE).

Level 2   the link access protocol which provides error free transporta-

85

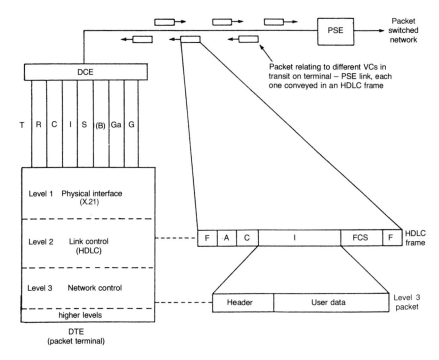

Figure 7.1   X.25 Interface Functions

tion of a packet over the (error prone) physical line between the DTE and the Packet Switching Exchange.

Level 3   The packet level which controls the traffic of the different virtual calls and multiplexes it for transmission as separate packets over the physical line controlled by Level 2.

LEVEL 1 – PHYSICAL INTERFACE (Figure 7.2)

This is specified as CCITT Recommendation X.21, the intention being that this should provide a common interface for accessing both packet and circuit switched networks. In fact, X.21 is designed for use on digital circuits that are not as yet widely available so, for an interim period, X.21 bis ('bis' means 'another version') which is compatible with the V.24/V.35 interchange circuits, as used by existing modem to terminal connections, can be used.

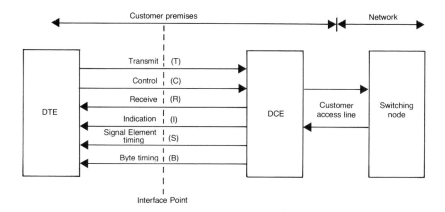

Figure 7.2 CCITT Recommendation X.21 – General Purpose DTE/DCE Interface for Synchronous Operation on Public Data Networks.

The X.21 interface is for synchronous terminals operating at 600, 2400, 4800, 9600 or 48,000 bits/s, and using IA5.

In some countries, in addition to bit timing, byte timing is provided as an additional option from the DCE. Including this option, eight X.24 interchange circuits are used. Associated with the Transmit circuit is a Control circuit which remains on for the duration of the call; associated with the Receive circuit is an Indication circuit which allows incoming signals from the network to be differentiated from incoming signals from the distant terminal. The other two remaining interchange circuits are a DTE common return and signal ground (or common return).

LEVEL 2 – LINK ACCESS PROCEDURE

The physical link established at Level 1 merely provides an undifferentiated stream of bits between the packet terminal and the PSE. To convey information across this link it is necessary to impose some structure on this bit stream. The High Level Data Link Control (HDLC) frame (Figure 7.3) is used to provide this structure.

The flag is arranged to be a unique 8-bit sequence, and once the flags have been detected the position of the other fields in the frame can be deduced.

Number of bits					
Flag	Address	Control	Information	FCS	Flag
8	8	8	variable	16	8

Figure 7.3   HDLC Frame

The HDLC frame serves as a mechanism for carrying a packet of data between the packet terminal and the PSE. The packet, complete with its header containing addresses, etc, is contained within the Information field of the HDLC frame.

Some means is required to overcome the effect of errors which can occur on the packet terminal-PSE link, and also to control the flow of information over this link. The HDLC protocol provides for both of these functions, using the Control field of the frame in conjunction with the Frame Check Sequence (FCS). The FCS is a polynomial error check which protects the Address, Control and Information fields of the frame.

The exchange and the subscriber DTE both acknowledge the receipt of frames passing the sum-check. Frames failing the sum-check are discarded and are subject to retransmission by the sender (ie the exchange or the DTE as appropriate).

The procedure is a little more complex than suggested here as several frames may be transmitted before an acknowledgement needs to be received, and additionally frames containing packets flowing in one direction carry acknowledgements in the frame header for frames going in the other direction.

This HDLC layer of X.25, layer 2, is known as the link access procedure; it provides a mechanism for managing the packet terminal-PSE link, and for transferring all packets between the packet terminal and the PSE.

Two link-level (level 2) procedures are defined in the recommendation: these are known as LAP and LAPB (Link Access Procedure – Balanced). LAP procedures were used on early public data networks. LAPB is the HDLC conforming procedure preferred by the CCITT as it provides symmetrical control and data transfer procedures, and simpler recovery rules.

For further details of the HDLC link control protocols the reader should refer to the CCITT 'Yellow Book' pp 104, and to the ISO documents 'International Standards 3309, 4335, 6159, 6256'.

LEVEL 3 – THE PACKET LEVEL

The level 3 of the CCITT Recommendation X.25 relates to the transfer of packets at the DTE/DCE interface. It requires each packet to be contained within the link level information field described earlier.

The further CCITT Recommendation (X.2) designates virtual call and permanent virtual circuit services as essential services to be provided by all networks. Datagram service is designated as an additional service which may be provided by some networks.

The description in the following sections concentrates primarily on the procedures for the virtual circuit service plus abstracts covering packet formats for all services and procedures/formats for optional user facilities.

For full information on the procedures for the datagram service, the reader should refer to the CCITT 'Yellow Book'.

Logical Channels

To enable simultaneous virtual calls and/or permanent virtual circuits and/or datagrams, logical channels are used. Each virtual call, permanent virtual circuit, and datagram channel is assigned a logical channel group number (less than or equal to 15) and a logical channel number (less than or equal to 255). For virtual calls, a logical channel group number and a logical channel number are assigned during the call set-up phase. The range of logical channels used for virtual calls is agreed with the Administration at the time of subscription to the service. For permanent virtual circuits and datagram channels, logical channel group numbers and logical channel numbers are assigned in agreement with the Administration at the time of subscription to the service.

Basic Structure of Packets

Every packet transferred across the DTE/DCE interface consists of at least three octets. These three octets (referred to as the packet 'header') contain a general format identifier and the logical channel group number, a logical channel identifier and a packet type identifier. Other packet fields are appended as required. Figure 7.4 illustrates the packet format.

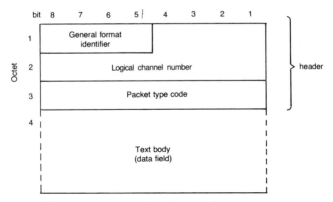

Figure 7.4   X.25 Level 3 Packet Format

The first octet contains the 'general format identifier' in bit positions 8, 7, 6, 5. The 'general format identifier' is a four bit binary coded field which is provided to indicate the general format of the rest of the header as shown in Table 7.1.

General Format Identifier	8	7	6	5
Call set-up packets	0	D	0	1
Clearing, datagram, flow control, interrupt, reset, restart and diagnostic packets	0	0	0	1
Data packets	Q	D	0	1
Datagram service signal packets	1	0	0	1

Table 7.1

Bit 8 of the general format identifier is used for the 'Qualifier' bit (Q bit) in 'data' packets, which is used to distinguish between control commands and user data for simple terminals connected to a PAD.

Bit 7 of the general format identifier is used for the 'delivery confirmation' bit (D bit) which is used to initiate a packet delivery confirmation procedure for 'data' and 'call set-up' packets.

Bits 5 and 6 are encoded to distinguish packets using modulo 8 sequence numbering from packets using modulo 128 sequence numbering (modulo 8 sequence numbering is shown in the diagram).

The logical channel group number appears in every packet (except 'restart' and 'diagnostic' packets) in bit positions 4, 3, 2 and 1 of the first octet. Eight groups of logical channels are identified: two for each of the four types of channels:

— permanent virtual circuits and datagrams;

— one way incoming;

— two way;

— one way outgoing.

The logical channel number appears in every packet (except 'restart' and 'diagnostic' packets) in all bit positions of the second octet. The third octet contains the packet type identifier. The packet types and their use in association with various services are shown in Table 7.2.

The various types of packets referred to above are described in the following description of procedures for virtual calls.

Packet type		Service	
From DCE to DTE	From DTE to DCE	VC	PVC
Call setup and clearing			
Incoming call	Call request	X	
Call connected	Call accepted	X	
Clear indication	Clear request	X	
DCE clear confirmation	DTE clear confirmation	X	
Data [and interrupt]			
DCE data	DTE data	X	X
[DCE interrupt]	[DTE interrupt]	[X]	[X]
[DCE interrupt confirmation]	[DTE interrupt confirmation]	[X]	[X]
Flow control and reset			
DCE receive ready	DTE receive ready	X	X
DCE receive not ready	DTE receive not ready	X	X
Reset indication		X	X
	Reset request		X
DCE reset confirmation	DTE reset confirmation		X
Restart			
Restart indication	Restart indication		
DCE restart confirmation	DTE restart confirmation		
Diagnostic*			

VC = Virtual Call   *Not necessarily available on all networks
PVC = Permanent Virtual Circuit

Table 7.2   Packet Types and their Uses with Various Services

PROCEDURES FOR VIRTUAL CALLS

X.25 provides two kinds of virtual circuits: permanent and switched. Permanent virtual circuits are defined at the time a DTE is first connected to the exchange. These may only be changed by prior notice and the change is effected at the exchanges involved. Switched virtual circuits (ie virtual calls) can be set up and cleared down as required. The mechanism for this was outlined earlier.

The procedures provided on each virtual circuit can be classified as follows (see Figure 7.5):

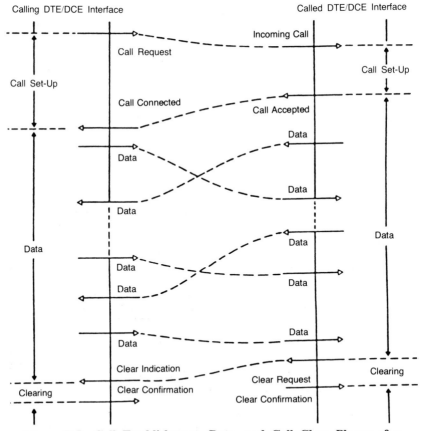

Figure 7.5   Call Establishment, Data, and Call Clear Phases of a Virtual Call

1   Call set-up and clearing;

2   Data transfer and interrupt (data packets and user control information);

3   Flow control;

4   Recovery (reset and restart procedures).

For permanent virtual circuits there is no call set-up or clearing procedure.

Call Set-up and Clearing (Figure 7.5)

In order to set up a virtual call the caller sends a 'call request' packet to the local exchange which is carried to the exchange in a frame at level 2. The packet contains:

— the chosen logical channel number (in the packet header);

— the address of the called party;

— indication of any optional network facilities chosen;

— up to 16 octets of user data.

A typical call request packet is shown in Figure 7.6.

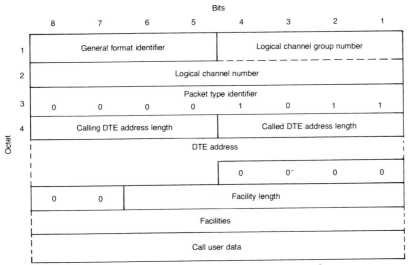

Figure 7.6   Format of Call Request Packets

Different networks may have different numbering plans (ie the way subscriber addresses are formatted). However, as national networks are likely to be inter-connected, CCITT propose that addresses are given in a standard binary coded decimal form, using four bits per decimal digit. Even so address lengths will vary according to whether the call is local or international. Networks may also offer 'abbreviated addressing' whereby a subscriber may address a few regularly used numbers by a shortened address sequence. For this reason the length of address (ie the number of digits) must be declared in the 'called DTE address length' field. A calling DTE may optionally include its own address, in which case its length must also be indicated in the 'calling DTE address length' field. Normally though this field has the value zero.

The caller may specify in the call request packet the optional user facilities shown in Table 7.3.

A full description of each facility is given in the CCITT Yellow Book; for illustrative purposes the following three examples are referred to in this description:

—   reverse charging;

—   priority class of traffic;

—   closed user group.

If reverse charging is requested, the called DTE will be charged for the call provided it subscribes to the facility and it accepts the call.

The priority class facility allows a DTE to select the priority class of traffic for a virtual call if this grade of service is required, eg incoming calls barred.

The closed user group facility allows subscribers to be members of a closed user group to which other subscribers may not have access. If this facility is being used, the facility field (see Figure 7.6) must contain a number of the closed user group to which the caller and the called DTE both belong, otherwise the call will not be processed.

The facility field is only presented in the call request packet if facilities are being requested. The length of this field must be declared in the 'facility length' field, even if zero.

Finally the caller may include in the call request packet up to 16 octets of user data which could for instance carry some user level identification for log-in purposes.

The called party receives an 'incoming call' packet, which has the same format as the call request packet. It differs in that the logical channel number will be that chosen by the network, and the packet will contain the address of the calling party. The facility field will indicate the facilities requested by the caller, and there will also be up to 16 octets of user data as sent by the caller.

If the call is accepted, the called DTE will return a 'call accepted' packet, and the caller will receive the 'call connected' packet which has the same format, but with the logical channel number changed to agree with that of the call request packet.

Non-standard default window size
Default throughput class assignment
Incoming calls barred
Outgoing calls barred
Single closed user group (CUG)
Single CUG with outgoing access
Single CUG with incoming access
Incoming calls barred within a CUG
Outgoing calls barred within a CUG
One-way logical channel outgoing
One-way logical channel incoming
Reverse charging
Reverse charging acceptance
Non-standard default packet size
Flow control parameter negotiation
Throughput class negotiation
Multiple closed user groups
Multiple CUG with outgoing access
Multiple CUG with incoming access
Extended packet sequence numbering
RPOA selection
Fast select
Fast select acceptance
Packet retransmission
Bilateral closed user group
Bilateral CUG with outgoing access

Table 7.3   X.25 Optional User Facilities Provided

If the call is not accepted by the called party, or if the original call request is invalid it may be refused by the network. In the first case the called party returns a 'call clear request' packet in response to the 'incoming call' packet; and in both cases the network will return a 'clear indication' packet to the caller, containing information why the call request is refused.

Either party may terminate a virtual call by sending a 'call clear request' packet, the network again delivering a 'clear indication' packet to the other party.

After receiving a 'call clear request' packet from a subscriber the network will reply with a 'call clear confirmation' packet in order to complete the freeing of the logical channel number.

Similarly a subscriber must return a 'call clear confirmation' packet to the network in response to a 'clear indication' from the network, again to complete the release of the logical channel.

Data Transfer and Interrupt (Figure 7.5)

Once a virtual circuit is established, either subscriber may send, and expect to receive, data packets which carry in the header the logical channel number corresponding to the virtual circuit in question. These packets may carry any number of octets of user data up to the maximum allowed by the network administration. Typically this will be 128 octets (1024 bits) but other maximum values may be offered by the network administrator.

The subscriber does not have to declare the length of packets, since each is conveyed to the exchange in a frame (level 2 of X.25) which flags the beginning and end of the transmitted packet. However, if the user data exceeds the locally permitted maximum, the network will reset the call.

In practice a short packet may pass into another network which offers a longer maximum length: however, packets from a network of the latter kind passing into the former may have to be cut into a number of shorter packets. This procedure is purely the province of the two network administrations concerned, and provided the correct order is maintained the receiving subscriber will merely receive several short packets instead of one long one.

However, it is possible that users may attach significance to packet boundaries. For example it may be desirable to get the whole of one message or transaction unit into one packet. If packet fragmentation occurs during the course of passage through the network, this can adversely affect the application. Therefore, X.25 provides a facility which allows for indication that the data stream logically continues in the subsequent packet (or packets). A bit called the 'more data mark' (Mbit) is set aside in the header of data packets (shown in Figure 7.7).

If a packet is fragmented, the network sets the 'more data' bit in each fragment except the last, to maintain complete packet sequences.

Thus the more data mark may be set by a sender to indicate that a message or logical sequence extends over more than one packet. A series of data packets with the more data mark set forms a logical sequence. This

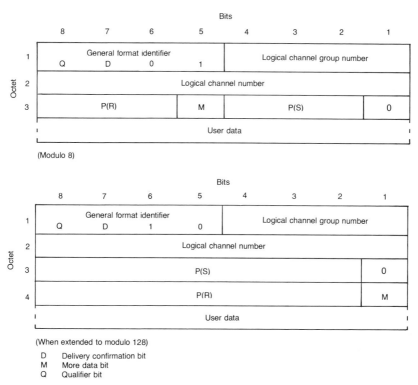

(Modulo 8)

(When extended to modulo 128)

D   Delivery confirmation bit
M   More data bit
Q   Qualifier bit

Figure 7.7   DTE and DCE Data Packet Format

is deemed to end with the transmission of a packet having the 'more data mark' clear.

The more data mark may only be set in packets which are of the maximum length for that network.

Messages passing between two subscribers will in general be either data or control information. Normally this distinction would be purely the province of the subscribers, but there are two circumstances in which it is convenient for the network to provide mechanisms by which users may pass control information to each other.

One relates to the exchange of information between a packet terminal and a simple terminal connected to a PAD. It is necessary to be able to distinguish between control messages and user data to and from the simple terminal using the PAD.

In data packets therefore another bit called the 'data qualifier' (Qbit) is set aside in the header. This bit is set to a 'one' for PAD control messages. Data packets destined to the terminal, or assembled by the PAD from the terminal have this bit set to zero.

The second control mechanism available in X.25 is called the 'interrupt' facility, and is provided by means of a special packet type. Data packets are subject to a flow control mechanism described below, which allows both the network and subscribers to regulate the rate at which the data packets on any virtual circuit may be transmitted and received. It is possible therefore for the flow temporarily to dry up on a call, thereby blocking the passing to the far end of the very control information which could relieve the situation. For example, if data packets have been sent to the network, and there has been no indication of an error or network malfunction but there has been no acknowledgement from the recipient, the result is impasse: you cannot find out what has happend without sending more packets, but you cannot send more packets until those outstanding have been acknowledged.

One has the option of resetting the call but this means resetting the data packet sequence numbers and may involve the loss of data packets already caught in the system. Use of the interrupt packet may avoid the need to do this, and thus may be preferable.

The user may therefore send an 'Interrupt packet' (as shown in Figure 7.8) bearing the logical channel number of the virtual call, which will by-pass all data packets in the network belonging to the call, and will be delivered to the other subscriber on his appropriate logical channel. This packet carries a single octet of user data which may be used to qualify the interrupt. The receiver must reply with an 'Interrupt confirmation' packet before the network will accept the transmission of another interrupt on that virtual call.

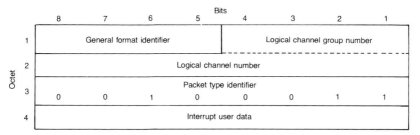

Figure 7.8   DTE and DCE Interrupt Packet Format

Flow Control

So far the explanation has shown that the receipt of packets through the network must be acknowledged. For example, the call request is answered by a call confirmation, the clear indication is answered by clear confirmation and Interrupt by Interrupt confirmation, etc. This simple mechanism provides flow control which prevents overload by not inviting fresh input until the previous transaction has been completed. It also ensures strict sequence control.

This is appropriate for the service packets of X.25 but would be unduly restrictive as a flow control mechanism for controlling data packets. Thus the protocol between the DTE and the exchange allows each to anticipate the acknowledgement of data packets by the other and to transmit several before an acknowledgement is received. To achieve this each data packet (see Figure 7.7) carries a number P(Sent) in the header which starts at zero for the first and is incremented for each successive packet.

A separate count is kept for each logical channel. Up to a predefined number of packets may be sent on a logical channel before a reply must be received. This is called the 'window', which is progressively 'closed' by the transmission of each packet, until, after the final packet, it is 'shut' and no more data packets may be sent to that logical channel until an acknowledgement is received.

The standard window size is two packets for each direction of transmission. In addition, other window sizes (up to 8 or 127 when extended) may be offered by administrations. Optional window sizes may also be selected for a period of time.

A special acknowledgement packet called 'receive ready' is used to acknowledge data packets. It comprises only a header, and carries a number P(Received) corresponding to the transmitted packet number P(Sent) which indicates that all data packets up to the number P-1 have been received and that the next packet expected will be the one numbered P. This acknowledgement reopens the shut or partially shut window, indicating that more packets up to the given number may be sent starting at the one numbered P.

Since the logical channel (and the virtual circuit it supports) can be used for data in both directions simultaneously, data packets in one direction between the DTE and the exchange can be used to acknowledge data packets flowing in the other direction. Thus a data packet carries in the header not only its own number P(Sent) but also the value P(Received) for the numbering sequence used in the other direction (as shown in Figure 7.7).

This cuts down the number of 'receive ready' packets that have to be sent and which otherwise carry no useful traffic. P only has values in the range zero to seven, the numbering sequence of packets being cyclic (modulo 8), ie the numbers are reused to identify new packets, as old packets are acknowledged.

Two other flow control packets are provided to help overcome more difficult situations. If the DTE or the exchange are temporarily embarrassed for space to receive new data packets, a 'receive not ready' packet may be sent which indicates that no more data packets should be sent.

It too carries an acknowledgement number P(Received) so that packets already received can be acknowledged. The instigator removes the hold condition by the transmission of a 'receive ready' packet on the appropriate logical channel.

Finally, if the DTE receives a packet with a number which is apparently not in sequence then it may send to the exchange a 'reject' packet in which the number P(Received) indicates the number of the packet that is expected. The exchange then backs up and recommences transmission of one or several consecutive data packets from that point.

Recovery Procedures

Despite all the precautions which are provided for in the implementation of the protocol, it is still possible for things to go wrong. When some failure somewhere in a DTE or an exchange leads to an ambiguous situation resulting in a failure in the data flow, fairly drastic action is required in the form of 'interrupt', 'reset' or 'restart' packets.

The 'interrupt' packet as described earlier may be used to restore the flow of data but if this fails then the first alternative is to reset the logical channel, and hence the virtual circuit, to its initial state. This is a much more drastic remedy than the interrupt procedure because reset removes all data and interrupt packets already in the network pertaining to the logical channel and resets the packet numbering sequences at each end; thus it is possible for data to be lost.

The resetting procedure is initiated by the DTE transmitting a 'reset request' packet or the DCE a 'reset indication' packet. Both packets contain the logical channel number in the header and also specify the reason for the reset and a diagnostic code in the text body.

When the receiver has taken the appropriate action by discarding packets and resetting counters, it replies with a 'reset confirmation' packet, at which stage the logical channel is placed in the 'flow control ready' state and the transfer of data packets may recommence; until the confirmation is received the exchange ignores 'data' and 'interrupt' packets on the logical channel in question.

In the event of a major problem a restart procedure may be initiated to re-initialise the packet level interface. This procedure is even more drastic than the reset because in this case all the virtual calls are cleared and all permanent virtual call channels reset. At any time the DTE may request a restart by issuing a 'restart request' packet or the exchange may indicate a restart by transferring a 'restart indication' packet across the interface. The receiver confirms the restart by issuing a 'restart confirmation' packet which 'clears' all the logical channels used for virtual calls and 'resets' all logical channels for permanent virtual circuits.

Collision of Packets

To minimise the chance of a terminal and its exchange simultaneously generating a 'call request' and 'incoming call' packet on the same channel, 'call requests' are made on the highest free logical channel number and 'incoming call' packets are received on the lowest. However, should a collision occur, the 'call request' packet will take precedence over the 'incoming call' packet, which will be discarded.

If 'clear request' and 'clear indication' packets collide the exchange will consider that clearing is complete, so clear confirmation will not be transmitted. If a 'reset request' and 'reset indication' packet collide the channel will revert to the Flow Control Ready state, so no confirmation packet will be necessary. If a 'restart request' and a 'restart indication' packet collide, all the logical channels used for virtual calls are cleared and all logical channels used for permanent virtual circuits reset.

USES OF X.25

Because X.25 provides the user with a protocol which supports multiple data conversations on a single link, a computer connection through an X.25 port can support the same number of logical channels as several port connections into the network but at a lower cost. The single X.25 link is also likely to save on the cost of the communications interface hardware on the user's equipment.

A common use of X.25 is therefore in the connection of computers to public packet switched data networks.

Another example of this line-sharing principle is often found in private communications networks using leased circuit connections. In applications such as airline reservations and on-line information retrieval large numbers of terminals are connected to host computers through the network. In many cases, the total volume of information sent and received is small. With the more traditional solutions, such private networks require expensive hardware additions to provide communication port connections to attach all of the many communications lines to the computer. With the X.25 solution a single front-end processor with one or more X.25 links to the computer can replace all of the individual terminal connections. In this example X.25 is not a networking requirement but instead is used as a concentration protocol either to save on the cost of computer ports or to allow the connection of more terminals than can physically be handled by the computer.

X.25 can also be used to connect computer systems together. For example many users are integrating their data processing operations through X.25 to provide both user and program access to databases resident on different computers often located at different sites and served by separate networks. Because X25 is an international standard, it is now being supported by most of the major computer companies and allows computers of different speeds, types and manufacture to be linked together. Also the multiple-channel capability of X.25 allows users to exchange data between several tasks at the same time and still support terminals on one system accessing programs or data, on another. Being full-duplex, X.25 can support simultaneous transmission in both directions thereby reducing the interference between users.

Very large users of computer services such as universities, research establishments, banks and other financial installations have combined many of these uses to create a private packet switched network.

To maximise the interworking capabilities between terminals and different hosts throughout private (and public) packet switched networks, a wide range of network products are used which provide X.25 concentration and network switching and connection. These devices are normally considered as a fully implemented mini network node and are used to build private packet switching data networks, such as shown in Figure 7.9. They function in the same way as nodes in a public network, making connections and routeing data amongst the various computers and terminals.

Private networks often span large geographical areas and usually combine private leased circuits and public data networks into the most cost effective arrangement. As an alternative to the traditional 'star' and 'multi-drop' networking, packet switching can often offer other advantages including the increased flexibility and reliability which is so important in the distributed networking systems of today. Such a network is often seen as offering free connectivity between users and at the same time providing the ability to define 'closed user groups' to restrict access to sensitive data.

For large volume networks, X.25 switch/concentrators enable cost-effective branch or subnetworks to be built which concentrate traffic from low volume areas into large capacity nodes or switching centres. This is shown in Figure 7.10 which illustrates a fully integrated public and private packet switched data network.

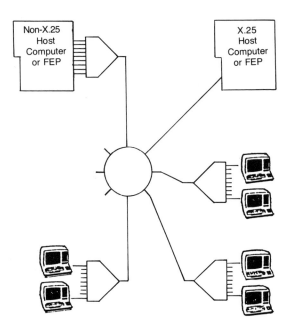

Figure 7.9   X.25 Private Network

In addition to its concentration and switching roles the use of an X.25 switch as a gateway between the public and private network provides a cost-effective means of sharing relatively expensive X.25 access lines with the public data networks. The interconnection of public and private networks in this manner is described further in the next chapter.

In several products the functions of X.25 network switching and concentration are combined with the PAD functions. For example, the CAMTEC JNT-PAD combines the functions of a PAD for connecting up to 16 asynchronous character terminals to X.25 based networks, with an X.25 switching and routeing capability on up to ten X.25 lines.

With the availability of at least two X.25 ports on the basic configuration, terminal access can be extended to the X.25 network or local host (see Figure 7.11). The host can also access the wide area network using the X.25 switching capability of the PAD.

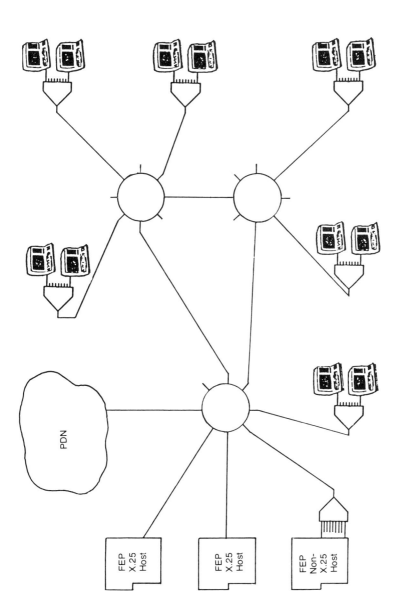

Figure 7.10 Fully Integrated Public and Private Packet Switched Data Network

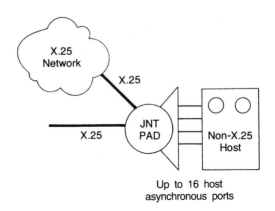

Figure 7.11   Use of X.25 PAD with Two Ports

The second X.25 port can also be 'daisy-chained' (cascaded) to one or more PADs to increase the number of terminals linked to a particular X.25 route (see Figure 7.12).

Often a leased line will provide the most cost effective link between the PAD and the host but for sites with relatively low volumes of data, the

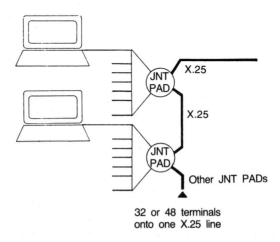

Figure 7.12   Daisy-chained PADs

option of connecting over PSS via the second port may be more cost effective. Also by using both a leased line and access to the PSS network, automatic re-routeing of calls in the event of line failure can be achieved with the alternate addressing facilities provided by the PAD.

Examples of the use of X.25 in many of these situations is illustrated in a look at specific applications of PSS and X.25 described in Chapters 12, 13 and 14.

HOST COMPUTER SUPPORT FOR X.25

The initial acceptance of X.25, especially in the USA, was slow because of the time necessary to develop support of the protocol by the major computer suppliers. This was chiefly due to the normal development cycle and also the extreme caution shown by a number of suppliers when faced with a new protocol standard such as X.25.

Today the major computer suppliers have largely embraced X.25 into their product lines. Further stages of enhancements have also been implemented by many of these vendors to integrate X.25 fully into their communications network products. As an illustration, Appendix 7 describes the way in which X.25 is supported in IBM products.

Some suppliers are also upgrading their support of optional facilities of X.25 to increase its application to specialised communications environments. Most of the suppliers of large mainframes will eventually support all of the facilities described in the 1980 revision of X.25.

An important consequence of having a standard interface is that it becomes practicable to implement it with hardware. Suppliers of LSI technology products have produced devices which simplify the processing required to implement X.25 by moving some of the logic onto a chip. Although implementations of level 2 of X.25 have been in existence for some time, until there is a uniformity of implementation of all components and in particular level 3, there will remain a requirement for some software elements.

This trend is resulting in direct X.25 support by simpler and low cost computers and terminals. Although it is unlikely that such devices will eliminate the need for a PAD function in the near future, in certain areas the availability of a relatively inexpensive packet-mode terminal becomes an attractive consideration.

Software is also available to provide X.25 support outside the areas where the computer supplier has elected to provide his own implementations. Although relatively expensive it is far less costly than custom-built implementations of X.25 and considerably reduces the development time needed to a fraction of that required for special X.25 programming efforts. This approach can help users with older computer systems which will not be upgraded to provide X.25 support but are required to operate in an X.25 environment.

All X.25 packages do not provide an equivalent level of support. Even though the protocol is standardised, variations in the features available can conflict with the requirements of public networks or other suppliers' products. In the selection of such products it is suggested that the following features should be examined for any restrictions and for the level of support provided for specific host computers:

— number of logical channels which may be assigned on a link;

— maximum speed of the line;

— support of X.29 PAD facilities;

— support of optional facilities, eg closed user group;

— operating system and application support for X.25;

— memory and other hardware requirements to support X.25;

— approval status;

— address length for international numbering;

— level of support implemented.

OTHER X.25 PRODUCTS

Most organisations using PSS will find that either X.25 host computer support or a 'private' PAD are the only X.25 products required to support their communications applications. For users with more extensive and complex X.25 networking requirements there are numerous other X.25 products available. These include:

— X.25 communications processors;

— front-end processors with X.25 software implementations;

— X.25 concentrators;

— X.25 multiplexers (private PAD functions);

— data analysers;

— protocol testers;

— protocol converters;

— software packages;

— protocol chips.

Further information on these various products can be obtained directly from the suppliers of packet switching technology and through the references given in the Bibliography (Appendix 1). Detailed descriptions of these devices are beyond the scope of this publication because they extend far beyond the field of public data networks. The exception is the Packet Assembler/Disassembler (PAD) which is discussed further in Chapter 9.

8 Interconnection of Public and Private Data Networks

INTRODUCTION

In countries where private data networks are permitted there is a growing requirement for their interconnection with public packet switching networks.

As the number and size of private data networks increase, the maturing system of national data networks with standard X.25 packet mode interfaces and international X.75 connections offers new opportunities for national and worldwide inter-communication.

X.25 concentrators have proved attractive in reducing the customer cost of terminal access to public networks and, when combined with switching capabilities, have enabled cost-effective networks and sub-networks to be built. More specifically, the use of an X.25 switch as a gateway between the public and private networks provides a cost-effective means of sharing relatively expensive X.25 access lines to the public data networks.

Public network access from private networks can provide increased geographic network coverage, provide extra network capacity on demand, or provide an alternative form of low-cost back-up to private circuits.

For small private networks requiring wide geographic coverage with low data volumes, long-distance transmission over public networks may be cheaper than dedicated facilities. For large networks dedicated connections on heavily used routes can be supplemented with public network switched connections to permit economical wide geographic coverage.

111

GATEWAY

The term 'gateway' is now commonly used to define a facility which interconnects two networks so that users on one network may communicate with users on another network. Figure 8.1 shows two typical gateway applications referred to in an earlier chapter. The Telex to PSS gateway (InterStream One) allows terminals on the public telex system to gain access to computers on PSS. The Telex to Teletex Conversion gateway (InterStream Three) allows Telex terminals to communicate with Teletex terminals which may be either on the telephone network, or on PSS.

The term 'gateway' is thus broad but here we are solely concerned with a 'gateway' which provides interconnection between private packet switching networks based on OSI principles and the public packet data networks based on the X-Series Recommendations.

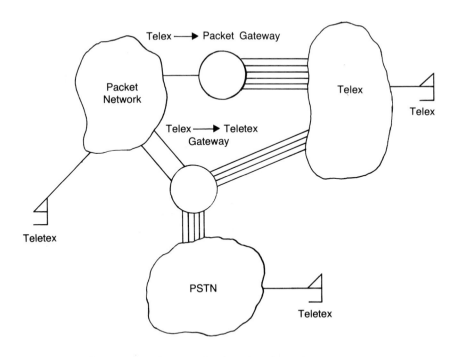

Figure 8.1   Gateways

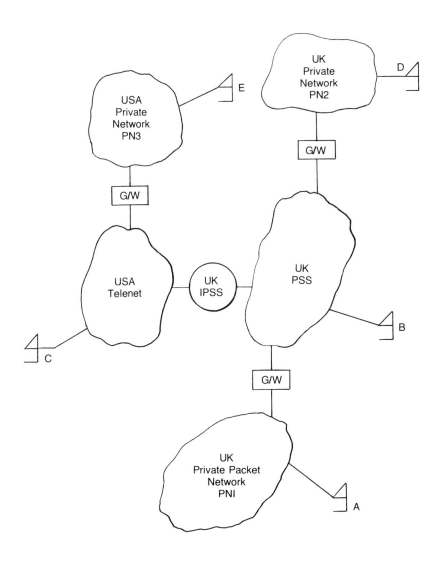

Figure 8.2 Connecting Private Networks to the Worldwide User Community

Figure 8.2 shows how private networks may wish to attach to public networks. For example a private network could have been installed to handle the major data communication requirements of the organisation but subsequently a need had arisen for secondary communication with users on other networks. In this example, this means that user A on private network PN1 may need to establish calls and communicate with users B, C, D and E on other networks. Conversely it means that those users are able to establish calls to and communicate with user A as well as each other.

There are two fundamental requirements of private-to-public network interconnection methods which need to be provided in gateways. First, universal accessibility for private network Data Terminal Equipment (DTE); and second, adequate cost control mechanisms for administration of the private networks.

Active discussion of private network interconnection is proceeding within the various international standards committees. X.25 is seen as the best protocol available to private packet switching networks but interconnection poses problems of addressing, routeing, availability and accounting that are beyond X.25 and must be resolved in the private networks.

Interconnection depends upon the method used to assign addresses to private network DTEs. The standards bodies have placed high priority on finding suitable private network addressing methods. Proposals for addressing extensions through the X.25 facility field and X.121 numbering plan extensions to permit private network addressing are under study.

Private network requirements initially have been met without any special interconnection mechanisms beyond X.25. There is a growing concensus of opinion that public/private network interconnection must be provided for and that X.25 is the appropriate protocol.

The ideal technical solution would be to directly attach private networks to the public services, thus becoming in effect a subset of the public network. However this does present both regulatory and practical difficulties.

CCITT Recommendation X.121 defines the international numbering plan for public data networks; it provides for international addressing within the 15 digit limit of X.25. Three or four digits (the DNIC) are used to identify the country, and possibly a network within the country. Up to 11 or 10 digits are available for use as national addresses. These are given significance and allocated by the network; on PSS they are structured as follows:

digits   5 –   7   area code

         8 – 12   terminal number

        13 – 14   sub-address digits (for use by the user)

In the case of PSS the top 12 digits of the 14 digit addresses (NUAs) are unique, the remaining two digits being available to the user.

If that user is in fact a private network there is an immediate problem of how calls originating on the public network are further routed through the private network. Three approaches to private network numbering which are compatible with X.121 have been proposed: shared address space, private local numbering, and private network national numbering. 'Shared address space' assigns addresses to private network DTEs within the numbering plan of a single public network; 'private local numbering' assigns DTE addresses that are chosen independently from the public network plan; 'private network national numbering' is similar to an integrated national numbering scheme except that one or more separate four-digit Data Network Identification Codes (DNIC) are assigned to cover all the private networks within a given country, and each private network has a nationally agreed Private Network Identification Code (PNIC). Although this is the basis of a draft amendment to X.121 a number of drawbacks exists:

— there is, as yet, no UK registration authority for number plans;

— there is doubt as to whether there is sufficient range of available numbers to accommodate the spread of private networks envisaged;

— the existing public networks do not support this facility.

Although there is currently no standard to define the services to be offered by a gateway, explicit standards for interconnection between private and public packet switching networks are actively under study. As mentioned earlier X.25 as presently defined can be used to provide standard gateways to public networks although the systems being implemented are usually application specific. For example, X.25

concentrators/switches can be effectively used as gateways between public and private networks.

In this role, X.25 gateways provide methods for the routeing and transmission of incoming and outgoing calls from or to a public data network. Both functions differ from previous uses of X.25 as a purely DTE/DCE protocol for public network access.

An incoming call from a public network can address a DTE on the private network using the sub-addressing feature of X.121. This means that the public network does not examine the entire destination address but passes all the information to the private network where further address analysis is carried out. Incoming calls from a public packet network to a private network are thus forwarded by the gateway to the private network terminal identified by the destination sub-address in the call packet.

Figure 8.3 illustrates a private network connected to PSS. In this example three computers (A, B, C) are accessed both remotely over PSS and locally via a private X.25 concentrator/switching device. A single dataline connection links the private network X.25 gateway to PSS and is assigned the address 707 12221.

A PSS user who wishes to access one of the computers would enter a Call Request packet from PSS with the 14-digit called address as follows:
      2342 707 12221 00

where '2342' is the PSS DNIC and '00' the sub-address.

The first 12 digits identify the trunk from PSS to the private circuit. The last two digits can be anything the caller types in. In this example, the routeing tables for the X.25 switch are set up such that the caller on PSS can call one of the three computers with the following numbers:

      707 12221 10 calls computer A

      707 12221 20 calls computer B

      707 12221 30 calls computer C

Use of a single X.25 circuit (or multiple circuits with the same public network address) permits world unique terminal numbers on the private network. Addresses on the private network conform to X.121 and lie within the range allowed by the public network. This is an example of 'shared address space'.

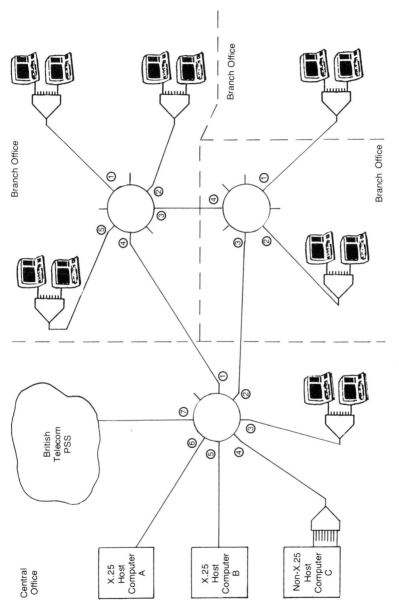

Figure 8.3 X.25 Network Application

Features are often provided on the gateway to modify address fields between the public and private networks to provide abbreviated terminal addresses within the private network as illustrated above. This enables sub-addressing from the public X.25 network to be translated into private network numbering schemes. A typical product will provide for 200 address entry possibilities each containing a single translation entry consisting of called address, translation address and usage counter. The gateway may also include public network charge facility information in the private network accounting data.

Outgoing calls can use international standard destination addresses to facilitate routeing with sub-addressing used to fully identify the destination. Outgoing calls from the private to public network use the same gateway but are routed to it by the X.121 DNIC. Although the gateway often supports load sharing and network administration features, the public network only sees an X.25 DTE and is not aware of the gateway function.

Although sub-addressing is supported on PSS this is not true of all public data networks; in these cases other techniques for assigning multiple consecutive addresses have been developed.

Where there are connections to multiple public data networks, the network manager chooses which DNICs to route via each network; at present the terminal user is not able to select transit network routeings.

Existing packet switching systems have the capabilities and features which provide the elements needed for interconnection. These include flexible routeing, multiple circuit services, call restriction options, accounting and flexible address formats. X.25 extensions are often provided including an option to permit 'call progress' signals from the DTE. Where allowed on the public network the 'call progress' signals are passed back by the gateway to indicate 'clearing' causes. This overcomes a weakness in the X.25 approach which arises from using DCE to DCE communication as against the normal DTE to DCE communication supported by X.25. The problem arises if the private network sends a 'Call Clear Request' packet because it is experiencing problems. If the packet has a diagnostic code which indicates a network fault then the public network may regard it as a protocol violation.

'YELLOW BOOK' TRANSPORT SERVICE AND TS29

Network addresses in an X.25 network are specific to that network and as such do not allow connections across more than one network to be set up automatically. This means that at present the terminal user is unable to select transmit network routeings, and as referred to earlier, where there are connections to multiple public networks the network manager must choose which DNICs to route via each network.

For private networks a similar problem existed particularly in the academic community where there has always been a pressing need to maximise interworking between a variety of terminals and different hosts connected over a number of networks.

In line with ISO protocols for Open Systems Interconnection (OSI) as described in Appendix 6, most networking applications will communicate via a 'transport service' interface (level 4 of the ISO Model) which is independent of the communications medium. The transport service separates the user from the details of the network such that minimal changes to application programs are required in order to work with different communications techniques. A major function of the transport service is to provide a global addressing technique for overcoming any deficiencies of the communications facility used, for example extending the two digit sub-addressing limitation of X.25 referred to earlier.

The 'Network Independent Transport Service' as defined by Study Group 3 (SG3) of the BT PSS Users Forum in document SG3/CP(80)2 (the Yellow Book) specifies the requirements of a transport service and the way in which these can be achieved using an X.25 network.

A number of gateway products support the address manipulation and basic end-to-end service primitives defined by the Yellow Book. Address manipulation is required to overcome the problem caused by each network allocating addresses to its own subscribers independently and without knowledge about addresses used on other networks. A call passing between more than one network must specify the appropriate gateway address to the first network and, once the call is connected, pass on as data the address to be used across the next network, and so on.

An annex to the Yellow Book details an implementation of the Transport Service over X.25 which enables the user to automatically set up and use a connection across multiple networks.

The Triple X (X.3, X.28 and X.29) protocols discussed in the earlier chapters of this book can only be used over X.25 based networks and depend upon specific features of the X.25 Recommendations.

To connect PAD terminals over the Transport Service, the Triple X dependency on X.25 is removed and a version of X.29 known as TS29 is used which communicates via the Transport Service. The encoding of TS29 over X.25 is specified in the 'Green Book' (see Appendix 5).

Further information on the progress, status and availability of standards at the transport and network levels of the OSI Model is given in Appendix 6.

9 Packet Assembler/ Disassemblers (PADs)

INTRODUCTION

The basic characteristics of packet switching are the transmission of data through a network in blocks (packets) rather than a character at a time. The packets are entered into the network using the network access protocol X.25. X.25 is the protocol for interfacing computers and intelligent terminals to a packet switched network and is suitable for devices capable of forming data into packets, ie packet mode terminals.

Packet switched networks are thus designed to support packet mode data terminal equipment (DTE). However, the majority of terminals available today still do not fall into this category. It is therefore recognised that if the full benefits of packet switching are to be realised by non-packet mode devices, then it is necessary to provide an X.25 emulator between the terminal and the network.

This emulator must be capable of initiating and responding to packet level procedures and of assembling data into packets for transmission across the network, and in the reverse direction, breaking the packets down into a data stream which the attached terminal understands. For this reason, such an emulator is more commonly referred to as a packet assembler/disassembler (PAD).

As shown in Figure 9.1 the PAD operates bidirectionally across the network, assembling packets of data received from the terminal for transmission over the network, and disassembling packets coming from the network into data for the terminal.

Thus where non-packet mode terminals such as a teletypewriter or simple VDU are to be connected to the network, help to form data into packets is provided by a PAD.

121

Non-packet mode terminals cover a fairly wide range of types and applications but in general can be categorised as follows:

— asynchronous start/stop character terminals such as the teletype-writer or 'dumb' CRT device referred to above;

— terminals and workstations operating in a point-to-point mode such as RJE;

— semi-intelligent devices operating in a block mode polled environment such as IBM 3270;

— specialised devices such as viewdata and word processors with their own protocol requirements.

Several packet network suppliers have developed products to support a relative narrow cross-section of devices from each of the above categories. However, at the time of writing PSS prior to the Multi-Stream launch supports only packet mode DTEs and asynchronous start/stop character terminals.

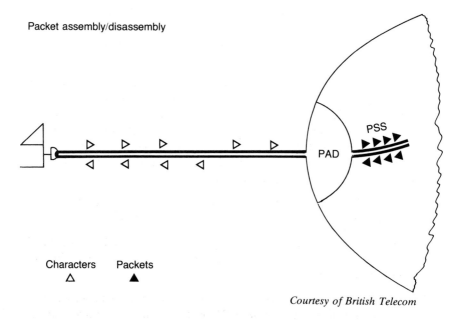

Packet assembly/disassembly

Characters   Packets
    △   ▲

Courtesy of British Telecom

Figure 9.1   Packet Assembler/Disassembler (PAD) Operation

This approach was adopted by BT because start/stop character terminals are the only type for which clear protocol recommendations had been made by the CCITT, ie the Recommendations X.3, X.28 and X.29.

SUPPORT FOR ASYNCHRONOUS TERMINALS

Recommendation X.3 defines a set of 18 parameters which specify the terminal's profile in the PAD. This includes parameters for defining terminal speed, echo facilities, packet forwarding conditions and handling capabilities such as line feed and line folding. These are discussed in more detail in a later section of the chapter.

Recommendation X.28 defines the way in which the asynchronous terminal accesses the PAD and controls user selectable facilities. It specifies procedures for character interchange, service initialisation, exchange of control information and the setting of the PAD parameters. For example, Recommendation X.28 allows a user to set up or clear virtual calls to a remote computer through the packet switched network.

Recommendation X.29 defines the way in which a remote packet mode DTE (for example a host computer) controls a PAD and exchanges data with it. Non-data messages sent over X.25 allow the host to read and/or set the PAD parameters and so control the host-to-terminal dialogue.

All X.29 information is embedded in the user data field of the X.25 packets (described in Chapter 7). Part of this information includes the 'protocol identifier' which uses the first 4 octets of the user data field in the 'call request' packet. X.29 defines the way in which control messages passing between the PAD and the packet mode DTE are distinguished from messages containing user data. This is achieved by setting the 'data qualifier' or 'Q bit' (described in Chapter 7).

Figure 9.2 illustrates the relationship between Recommendations X.3, X.28, X.29 and X.25 in a packet network environment.

These recommendations were adopted by the CCITT in the 1980 plenary session. The recommendations of the 1984 plenary Assembly are outlined in Appendix 8.

For a PAD capable of converting asynchronous protocols into a form suitable for transmission over an X.25 packet network, the major functions can be summarised as follows:

— the assembly of characters from the terminal into packets for the packet mode DTE;

— the disassembly of the data fields of packets into characters for the non-packet mode DTE;

— the setting up, interrupting, resetting and clearing of virtual calls and the generation of PAD service signals for the terminal;

— the forwarding of packets under specified conditions (buffer full, timeout expired, detection of control characters specified at PAD set-up);

— the recognition and interpretation of an interrupt or break signal from the terminal;

— the provision of appropriate flow control (enables terminals of different speeds to inter-communicate).

The following sections of this chapter provide a closer look at many of these functions by examining the operation and practical implementation

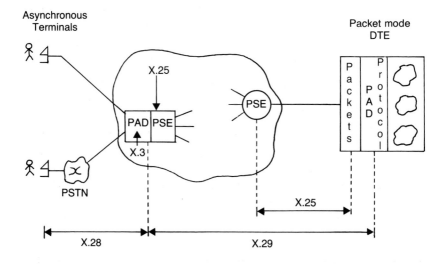

Figure 9.2   Relationship between Recommendations X.3, X.28, X.29 and X.25 in a Packet Network Environment

of PADs. From this emerges guidance related to the use of Recommendations X.3, X.28 and X.29. More specific recommendations on the use of X.3, X.28 and X.29 to support character terminal access via PSS are given in the BT PSS User Forum 'Green Book' which is outlined in Appendix 5. Currently these are the interim recommendations for character terminal protocols to operate over the ISO Session Service (see Appendix 6) issued by the Focus Committee on IT Standards.

In addition to providing guidelines for implementors of software on host systems to support character terminal access via PSS, the 'Green Book' Recommendation also considers character terminal access on private networks connected to PSS (as discussed in Chapter 8), and the design of 'private' PADs which are described later in this chapter.

Over the years many organisations in the UK have implemented the Triple-X protocols to support character terminal access via PSS. The two main documents which define and explain these protocols are the PSS Technical Users Guide referred to in Chapter 3 and the 'Green Book' recommendations prepared by Study Group 3 of the BT PSS User Forum.

During the course of implementation, some deficiencies in these documents have come to light. To rectify this situation the Character Terminal Implementors Group of British Telecom's New Networks Technical Forum has produced 'Design Notes for PAD Implementors' as an attempt to discuss and clarify some of these issues.

The notes are based upon a collection of papers which have been submitted to the CT Implementors Group since its inception in 1981. They are intended to provide assistance to implementors in pointing out likely problems and pitfalls, and in proposing possible solutions to them.

The document, which was first published in March 1984, is not intended to be a static object; additions will be made to it as more information becomes available. The contents of the 1984 issue is given in Appendix 9 of this book.

PAD Parameters

The PAD is a flexible device which can be instructed to respond in different ways for different terminals according to the setting of the appropriate parameters.

There is a PAD at every PSS exchange and character terminal users have a wide degree of control over the way in which it handles their calls through the setting of the following PAD parameters:

1 Escape from Data Transfer State
2 Echo
3 Data Forwarding Characters
4 Data Forwarding Timeout
5 Ancillary Device Control
6 Suppression of PAD Service Signals
7 Action of the PAD on receipt of the Break Signal from the Character Terminal
8 Suppression of data delivery to the Character Terminal
9 Padding after CR (Carriage Return)
10 Line Folding
11 Terminal Speed (a 'read only' parameter)
12 Flow Control by Character Terminal
13 Line Feed Insertion After Carriage Return
14 Padding Inserted After Line Feed Character
15 Editing
16 Character Delete Character
17 Buffer Delete Character
18 Display Character

To accommodate the different terminal configuration requirements, the PAD parameters may be set specifically for any call and may be controlled either from the local character terminal using X.28 procedures, or by the packet mode device (eg host computer) being called. Although the X.29 procedures would normally be applied between a PAD and a packet mode DTE, the recommendation will apply equally for PAD to PAD connections which are described later.

However, for the convenience of the terminal user on PSS a set of parameter values called the 'terminal profile' is recommended for use with a particular terminal. These are sets of pre-arranged values for each parameter which unless overridden will automatically control the way in which the PAD operates and fills packets for the terminal. For example, the PAD may send a packet to the network whenever it receives the 129th character, ie when the buffer is full, after a given timeout has expired, or on detection of a control character, ie carriage return. This means that packets could be anything from full to nearly empty, eg containing a single word or character.

Differences of this nature can have a considerable effect on the level of usage charges incurred. For this reason PAD parameters are flexible and under the control of the terminal user.

Most users will find that one of several terminal profiles is recommended for use with a particular terminal. These are indicated to the PAD by a very simple command, eg D1 is frequently used for VDUs and A2 for teletypewriters.

The level of usage charges can also be affected by the remote packet device changing the PAD parameters of a character device. Although this would only apply under exceptional circumstances because normally a host computer chooses an optimum set of values, it may be useful to check for any changes made by the host being called. In addition to being able to call for a read-out of PAD parameters while a call is in progress, the 'call information' facility at the end of each data call provides information on the call duration and number of segments transferred.

Editing is available to character terminals to allow for correction of text errors by the terminal user. This facility allows individual characters or a complete packet to be deleted provided it is still held on the PAD. In certain circumstances the 'profile' imposes conditions on the editing facility.

Unusual PAD parameter settings may be encountered or required in certain cases on international calls. For example, the editing facility will often be disabled by the distant host.

Many terminals have an echo facility to increase the reliability of operation by echoing characters back from the host. Given a high degree of error free transmission on the PSS network it should only be necessary to echo from the PAD. This not only makes it easier to see when local transmission errors occur, but avoids attracting additional traffic charges through echo characters being treated individually as packet segments within the network.

If incoming data to the terminal does not contain a carriage return signal at the appropriate place it is possible for data to be lost because the line length of the terminal is not sufficient to accommodate the data being sent. The PAD parameters can be set to overcome this situation by inserting a 'format effector' character into the data stream after a certain number of characters have been counted; this technique is referred to as 'line folding'.

Communications between Asynchronous Terminals and the PAD

Access between the asynchronous character terminal and the PAD may be gained over a PSTN or dataline connection to PSS (see Chapter 3). For dial-up connection over PSTN the user is allocated an NUI which is a password into the network and also identifies the user for accounting purposes.

Recommendation X.28 specifies the protocol to be used between an asynchronous character terminal and the PAD. It lays down procedures for:

—   establishing a call to the PAD from the terminal;

—   setting the PAD parameters to the required values;

—   exchanging data between the terminal and the PAD.

Once the modem to modem connection has been established between the terminal and the PAD, the PAD is in the 'waiting state'. This state exists when the communications channel is active but before a call has been set up; to indicate that the channel is active the modems exchange binary signals. In this state the terminal user may set and/or read the PAD profile or any of the PAD parameters individually. On dial-up, the waiting state is limited to a period of two minutes; unless a call is set up during this period the PAD will disconnect. This does not apply to character dataline terminals where the waiting state continues as long as the terminal is connected.

For dial-up access into PSS a call is set up by sending a 'Service Request' signal from the terminal. This takes the form:

[CR] [CR] Terminal ID [CR].

That is, carriage return twice followed by the 2-character Terminal Identifier determined by the type of terminal; for example, D1 for VDUs and A2 for teletypewriters.

A2 or D1 are two of the 20 standard profiles which set the 18 parameters and therefore determine the type of terminal requesting the connection.

The above sequence must be completed within 30 seconds of receiving the call connected tone. The PAD responds to the 'Request for Service' by displaying the PAD and port number to which the connection is established:

eg LON/A02 – 19201059.

Character dataline users initiate the 'Request for Service' by pressing carriage return [CR].

Dataline users now key N–[CR] and dial-up users N[NUI][CR] using the NUI which has been allocated by PSS.

PSS acknowledges receipt of the NUI by asking for the NUA (Network User Address) of the called party. All users enter A[NUA][CR] for a UK host or A9[NUA] [CR] for an international host.

The PAD sets up the virtual call end then begins to carry out its packet assembly/disassembly functions. PSS confirms that connection has been established by displaying NUA+COM (the NUA plus COM).

At this point the user would enter into a normal data transfer state with the remote host. The call is terminated by either entering the host's log-off procedure or by keying [CTRL/P] CLR [CR]. PSS acknowledges 'log-out' and confirms call clear with a list of call duration time and number of segments received and sent.

After clearing from one call, another can be made by repeating the above procedure starting with N–[CR] for dataline users and N[NUI] [CR] for dial-up users. To avoid starting all over again with the log-on procedure, it may be easier to clear the first call (by entering two commands) and return the PAD to the waiting state referred to earlier, so that the next address can be entered straightaway.

During the data transfer phase of the virtual call the terminal can recall the PAD in order to alter the PAD parameters, reset or request the status of the virtual call, send an interrupt to the packet terminal, or clear the call.

A 'waiting for command' state is entered to allow communication with the PAD during the data transfer phase. This is usually done by keying CTRL/P or by pressing the 'break' key. With the PAD in this state, commands can now be entered as above; the sequence must be completed within 30 seconds before the PAD returns to the data transfer state.

Communications between a Packet Terminal and the PAD

The establishment of a virtual call from the PAD to the remote packet mode DTE (eg host computer), and flow control during the virtual call, follow normal X.25 procedures. What Recommendation X.29 does is specify the way in which control information and user data is exchanged between the PAD and the remote host. All this X.29 information is embedded in the user data field of the X.25 packets. Part of this information includes the 'protocol identifier' which includes the terminal profile and the speed of operation of the terminal. In 'call request' packets transmitted by the PAD the first four octets of the user data field become the protocol identifier thereby limiting the user data field to 12 rather than the 16 octets of the normal call request packet (see Chapter 7).

There are three types of control message which the packet mode DTE host computer can send to the PAD:

— it can set and/or read the PAD parameters;

— it can cause a 'break' signal to be sent to the character terminal;

— it can request clear-down of the call.

X.29 defines the way that control messages passing between the PAD and the packet mode DTE are distinguished from messages containing user data. This is done by setting the 'data qualifier' bit (Q bit) to 1 for control messages, and 0 for data messages (see Chapter 7).

Apart from these two differences in the packet formats used in communications between a packet mode DTE and a PAD, and normal X.25 procedures, in PSS the following restrictions apply:

— minicall request packets (see Chapter 3) which have a user data field of up to 128 octets are reduced to 124 octets when addressing a PAD;

— the PAD does not negotiate packet and window sizes (see Chapter 3) and therefore will always operate with a window size of 2 and a packet size of 128 octets.

In addition, the interrupt procedure is slightly modified when a PAD is involved. If a PAD receives an interrupt from the remote end, it returns a confirmation packet to comply with the protocol (see Chapter 7) but does not inform the local terminal. The terminal therefore sees the interrupt as a break in transmission.

Private PAD Configuration – Single Terminal

Asynchronous user terminals can be connected to the PSS network either via the PAD located remotely at the PSS exchange or, alternatively, via a 'private PAD' installed at the user's own premises and connected to the network via an X.25 dataline as shown in Figure 9.3. This enables terminals to be connected in-house and allows asynchronous terminals to access PSS as a packet mode terminal.

The in-house option has the advantage in that the error correction features of the network provided by the X.25 level 2 protocol are extended from the network into the user's premises. Asynchronous terminals do not normally have in-built error correction facilities and error

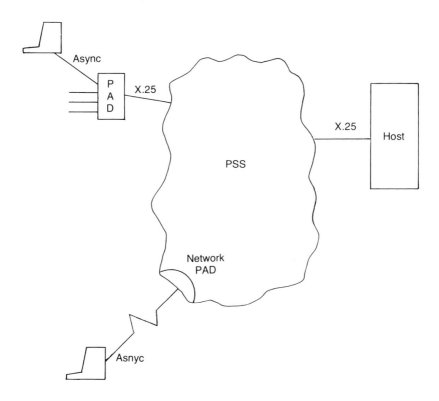

Figure 9.3   PAD Configurations

control is not provided by the network over the local dial-up or character dataline connection. Considering that the local PSTN is very much exposed to noise, vibration and interference conditions, which are not normally acceptable for good data communications, then the above option is particularly attractive from an efficiency point of view.

However, the user of an asynchronous terminal pays for the PAD function as part of the network usage charges whereas with a private PAD option additional charges are incurred in the cost of the PAD itself (typically £2K – £3K) and the X.25 dataline annual rental and connection charge (eg Dataline 2400 – £375 rental per quarter, £450 connection charge).

There is therefore a premium to be paid for error correction back to the user's premises. However dependent upon traffic usage, some of this additional cost can be offset by savings on local dial-up call charges over PSTN connections. In considering this requirement a user needs to examine his sums which should include the number of calls made, the length of each call, and the distance between the site and the network exchange (PSE).

On costs alone, it is most unlikely that the private PAD dataline option will be justified particularly because of the dataline cost involved in the connection; it is then really a question of deciding whether the lack of error correction facilities are acceptable for the application under consideration. It is also worth noting that private PADs, as we shall see later, provide faster and easier access procedures which overcome the 'unfriendliness' of the PSS network access procedures which were illustrated in the previous section.

Although this is the situation today, the imminent launch of the Multi-Stream protocols described in Chapter 5 will affect future thinking in the provision of local access facilities. In particular, the EPAD minimises the lack of protection of data and the CPAD the unfriendliness of access procedures. The one and four virtual circuit X.25 subsets also offer more cost-effective alternatives for the single-user workstation with the full benefits of X.25.

Products

A typical single port PAD such as the Dynatech Monopad allows one character mode terminal to access a public data network or private packet switching systems as a packet mode terminal. The PAD conforms to X.25, X.3, X.28, X.29 and X.121 standards and is fully compatible with public data networks Transpac, PSS, Datex-P and Telenet, etc.

The Monopad is PROM based and default parameters such as X.3 profiles and logical channel assignment are factory selectable. All 18 X.3 parameters are supported and 2 default profiles for either terminal or host are available. Fixed speeds are selectable up to 9600 bps, over the asynchronous channel with autobaud up to 1200 bps; 1200/75 bps is available as a factory option. The PAD facilities include remote addressing facilities which are user friendly, that is mnemonic addressing is used in which names and not numbers are typed in by the user.

The price to be paid for full error correction back to the terminal, and more friendly and faster access to the PSS network, is around £1500 for the Monopad, plus the charges for the dataline.

The Monopad is available in boxed form for attachment to the terminal or as an OEM card version for installation in the terminal or microcomputer, etc. This follows an increasing trend to build in X.25 ports in such devices; for example the IBM PC can be fitted with an X.25 card at a cost similar to that of the Monopad (see Chapter 12).

Private PAD Configuration – Several Terminals

The PAD can exist as a 'black box' which allows just a single terminal as described above to connect to the network. Alternatively, it can exist as a PAD/data concentrator connecting a number of asynchronous devices into the PSS network via a single-speed X.25 connection.

For a user with two or more terminals, an X.25 PAD remotely located from the network becomes extremely cost effective, when serving the dual role of packet assembler/disassembler and concentrator, as it permits multiple terminals to share a single high-speed connection into the network instead of a proliferation of low-speed connections.

The application of the PAD in this situation is usually to reduce costs where there are a number of users on the same site each incurring dial-up charges and, through X.25, to overcome the problem of no control over calls and the unfriendliness of the PSS network. It is quite common to install a point-to-point link with a statistical multiplexer and then upgrade to a PAD/multiplexer on moving to X.25.

Products

The Gandalf PIN 9101E is an X.25 network interface multiplexer designed to provide access to X.25 packet switched networks for up to 16 asynchronous devices.

The PIN 9101E is based on statistical multiplexer hardware but uses different software in operation as an X.25 network interface. It provides a single composite interface for connection to a node in a public or private packet switched network. On the multiplexer side it is an X.25 PAD which supports X.28, X.29, X.3 and in addition provides support for other local parameters not defined by X.3, that is extensions to X.3.

In Figure 9.4 the PAD is shown being used as a concentrator or multiplexer to interface a number of terminals to the network. The PAD is connected to the network via a single X.25 link and the host computer is also connected via an X.25 link. In addition to the terminals connected to the PAD, an asynchronous terminal is shown connected to the integral network PAD.

The terminals connected to the PAD may set up calls to any point on the network; ie, they can connect to the host computer, the terminal on the network PAD, or any other location. Similarly any terminal on the network can make a call to the host computer; several calls are simultaneously multiplexed over the single X.25 link to the host; each call is assigned to a logical channel or virtual circuit.

The PAD hardware comprises an input/output board for the asynchronous channels and a CPU board which carries out the packetising using PAD and X.25 functions. The CPU board provides a full X.25 specified link; the software is stored in PROM and is varied slightly to accommodate the changes required to suit each PTT's interpretation of X.25.

The asynchronous channels' characteristics are set at the beginning of each call according to parameters previously entered via an operator channel, or via an X.29 message from a remote DTE. In addition, a terminal user can configure his own channel parameters using the X.28 procedures.

Channels can be configured for generating calls, receiving calls or both. This enables the PAD to be used for concentrating terminals into a network as described above, and as we shall see later, as a front-end

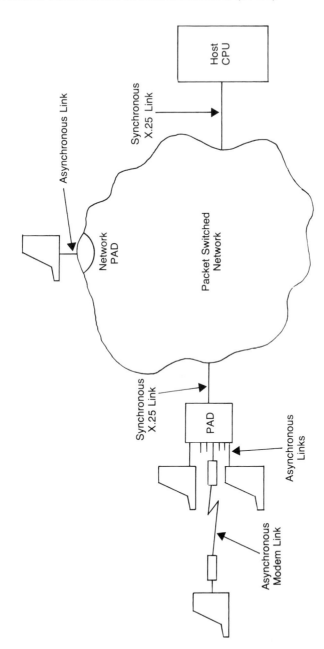

Figure 9.4 PAD used as the Interface between a Group of Terminals and a Host Processor

device to interface asynchronous computer ports to the network.

Any channel can be configured by the user as a DTE or a DCE by orientating a plug on the input/output module. For either configuration the PAD supports one or more RS232C connect protocols which allows the PAD to determine if the terminal equipment is connected to the channel and is ready to generate and/or receive a call.

In PSS operation, Recommendation X.3 sets the channel speed; with the PIN 9101E. The speed can be fixed or can be automatically adjusted using an autobaud facility, to match the terminal speed for each call. The autobaud feature is available for each of the 16 channels at speeds up to 9600 bps. When an autobaud channel has completed its connect protocol, the PAD waits for an autobaud character from the terminal equipment (usually carriage return) which is used by the PAD to determine speed and character sets. This facility is particularly useful where a wide variety of terminals is connected to the network through either a PABX or a data switch as described later.

Using the operator channel simple English language dialogue enables configuration parameters to be individually set for each channel and allows control over system parameters. The standard set of X.3 parameters and extended X.3 parameters may be configured by the operator. The support for other local parameters not defined by X.3 include:

— type of flow control;

— definition of X-ON, X-OFF, ENQ and ACK characters;

— parity generation (parity bit to user terminal);

— number of stop bits appended to transmitted character;

— autobaud enable/disable;

— autobaud speed limit;

— enforced reverse charging;

— individual channel enable/disable.

All parameter information is protected against loss due to power failure by battery back-up.

To simplify the PSS access procedures an abbreviated addressing feature allows the user to enter a 3-character mnemonic instead of the numeric address. Each name is equated to the X.25 network address (up to 16 digits) and, optionally, a 12 character User Data Field. When a terminal user enters the abbreviated address name during call generation the PAD will automatically set up a call request to the defined address or UDF.

During periods of peak activity, ie high user data input/output and/or retransmission of packets, a large buffer memory is used for data storage until normal flow is re-established. Flow control signals are provided for management of the buffer memory; control may be either via 'Clear to Send' or by transmission of X-ON/X-OFF characters. These characters may be coded as required via the Operator Channel to suit the attached devices.

Private PAD Configuration – Front-End Device

As the PAD can be configured either for generating calls, receiving calls or both, it can be used for concentrating terminals into the network (as described in the previous section) or for front ending a host computer to the network, or both. As a front end the PAD's function is to interface asynchronous computer ports to the network.

Figure 9.5 shows a PAD used as both a terminal concentrator and as a front end for several CPUs. The operation as a terminal concentrator is the same as described earlier and provides for calls to be set up at any point in the network.

The PAD which is shown functioning as a front end normally accepts calls from the network, goes through a short dialogue with the terminal user to determine the type of port required, and then connects the call to the appropriate port. In the example shown, local terminals are also connected to the front end PAD which as such functions both as a front end and terminal concentrator at the same time.

Referring to Figure 9.5 the normal data transfer operation is for a terminal user to type his data which is then assembled by the terminal concentrator PAD and formatted into an X.25 packet. The PAD transmits the data when a packet forwarding condition is encountered (usually a carriage return or a timeout).

The network routes the packet to its final destination, in this example the host connected via the front-end PAD. The front-end PAD receives

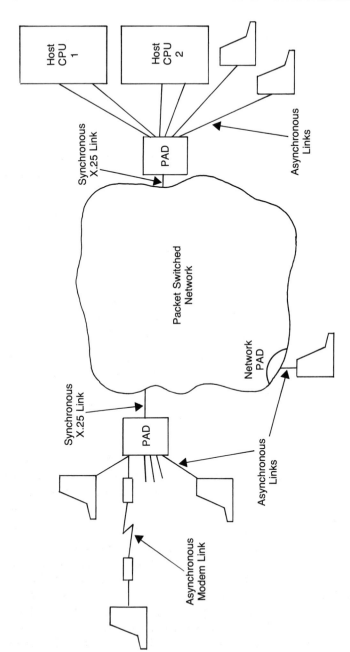

Figure 9.5   PAD Interfaces both Terminals and Host CPUs to the Network

the packet and outputs it to the asynchronous port to which the call was assigned where the entire packet of characters (usually a single line of data) is received by the host. The same process is followed in reverse order when the host has data to send to a terminal.

With this type of arrangement the normal echoplex operation from a terminal to CPU is not recommended. This is because each character would have to be formatted as a packet, transmitted to the host and then echoed back in the same way, thereby incurring all the X.25 overheads and network charges. Instead, host computers should be configured for non-echo operation and the front-end PAD should be configured to echo to the local terminal.

It is often advantageous to be able to program the X.3 parameter settings of the call originator from the call receive end during call set-up. For example, it might be desirable to change the data forwarding, flow control, or editing parameters to minimise data transmission costs or to accommodate the requirements of the user terminal.

Figure 9.6 shows a number of terminals connected directly to network PADs. These terminals may have different characteristics from each other for example different speeds, parity, flow control, etc.

In normal network operation each PAD parameter would have to be set manually by the terminal user to match his terminal characteristics using the X.28 procedures. More usually, control messages sent over the X.25 connection between the terminal and the host allow the host to read and/or set the PAD parameters and so control the host-to-terminal dialogue via X.29 procedures.

With front-end devices such as the Gandalf PIN 9101E, the X.29 function can often be extended by use of a 'Terminal Identity' facility. This facility enables programming of the X.3 parameter settings of the call originator (the terminal) from the call receive end (the host) during call set-up and provides automatic down line loading of X.3 parameters.

The terminal user simply calls the front-end PAD and if the 'Terminal Identity' function is enabled, the PAD interrogates the terminal identity. The user responds with a predefined 3-character 'terminal type'. When the PAD receives the packet, it checks that the 'terminal type' is valid and then, after discarding the packet, looks up the 'terminal type' in its internal tables and down loads the corresponding profile to the network PAD or private PAD via X.29. Alternatively the PAD may be

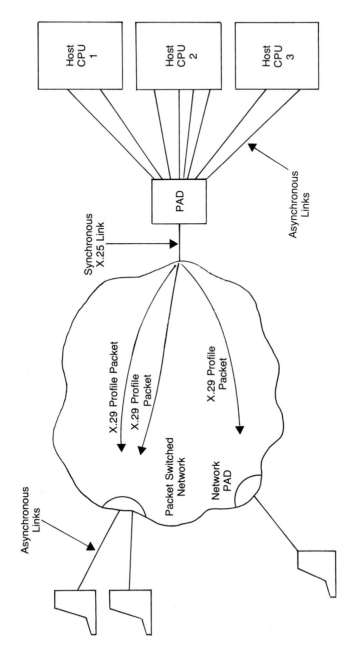

Figure 9.6   PAD used as Interface between Host CPUs and the Packet Switched Network: Automatic Configuration of Terminal Profiles

configured to automatically down load a predefined profile without prompting for a name. The Operator channel is used to define new 'terminal types' or to change the parameter values for each type at any time.

In many computer systems the services provided often fall naturally into two or more categories. Within a given category all the channels at the host end are connected to the same computer or service and users receive equivalent service regardless of which specific host channel is used. For example, a group of channels could be connected to an IBM system for one type of service, and another group to a DEC system providing a different service.

A 'Service Identity' function, available on devices such as the 9101E when used a a front-end PAD, permits the call originator to choose the desired services during the call connection process. The function is pro- grammed through the operator channel by grouping a number of chan- nels together and assigning the group a 3-character alphanumeric iden- tifier. PVC channels can be used but cannot be assigned a 'Service Identity' because a PVC is dedicated to a specific channel.

Remote terminal users simply request the desired service by entering the identifier when prompted during the connection procedure. If the identifier is valid the PAD attempts to connect the call to an inactive channel from among those assigned to the identifier. If successful, the PAD sends a message to the user equipment on that channel and informs the caller. If unsuccessful, the PAD informs the caller and clears the call. On the 9101E, 16 service identifiers are available either as service channels or as groups in contention (group hunting).

Private PAD Configuration – Local X.25 Gateway

In larger communications systems, greater flexibility and efficiency can often be achieved when PADs are interfaced with terminals through contention and switching systems (data switch or data PABX) as shown in Figure 9.7.

In effect the X.25 interface multiplexer (PAD) acts as a 'gateway' from the user's local network to the X.25 network. Typically up to 16 asyn- chronous communications channels can be interfaced with an X.25 pac- ket switching network such as PSS, using a single synchronous link. Within the communication network the X.25 gateway provision expands

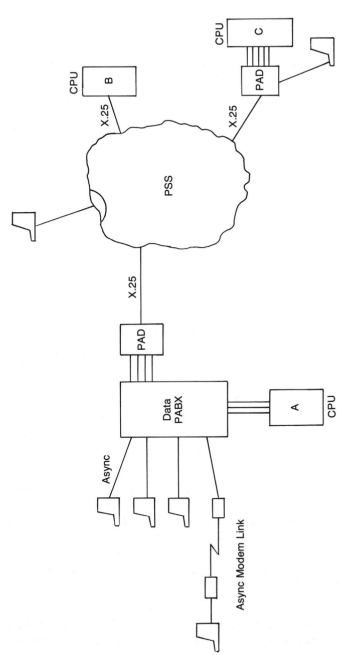

Figure 9.7 PAD used as Local X.25 Gateway with Data PABX

the contention capability of the data switch to include access to remote as well as local computer resources.

On receiving a connection request from the data switch, the X.25 gateway automatically generates a call to the network. Terminals (or hosts) can contend for the channels on the gateway which, in turn, transparently establishes connections through the network. In the configuration shown, any local terminal can be connected to host A, host B or host C. Remote terminals dialling into the data switch can be connected to host B or host C through the network, or to host A through the data switch; such an arrangement provides for considerable communications flexibility.

Cost savings from configuring a data switch network to include an X.25 interface result from the replacement of multiple dedicated modems and/or dial-up modems by a single transmission link and network charges which are related to traffic volumes rather than connect time. Additional benefits result from error-free communication achieved by the X.25 error detection and correction techniques used by the network.

Private PAD Network Management Facilities

To assist the network operator, X.25 interface units are provided with diagnostic capabilities to allow verification of hardware functions. Individual channel test routines can be run on-line under the control of the operator and the results displayed at a console terminal; diagnostics include error log, loop back, self test, etc. These facilities are aimed at assisting the operator in resolving the traditional third-party dilemma which often occurs in fault situations.

Network management information is usually provided in the form of a statistical log which is output via the operator's channel at the conclusion of each call and includes time, calling address, number of packets received and transmitted, call duration and number of resets. These statistics can either be accessed as and when required or a permanent printed record can be produced as a real-time log. In addition, an error log is often provided which reports timeouts, rejected frames, reset/restart conditions, link status and loss of data on the X.25 link.

Additional facilities are often included to assist in network configuration and operation. In the Dynatech Multipad X.25, for example, a software diagnostic port is provided which can be accessed by any port on the PAD or across the network from a remote location as a normal X.25 call. This port allows the operator to configure or reconfigure the PAD and its ports or to examine the state of the PAD and its trunk either locally or remotely. This means that users can be supported remotely and therefore minimises the amount of users' interference with the service. For example, day-to-day requirements such as speed changing can be handled by the operator centrally.

With the facility to set up PAD parameters remotely, once a PAD is installed on the network and connection provided by BT, then the installation can be remotely configured over PSS by the central operator and then monitored for performance using the fault checking diagnostics on the port, etc.

As well as being useful to the network operator, the software diagnostic port is used by several suppliers as part of their customer fault finding service because it enables them to check out devices without visiting the site.

Although these facilities are often provided as part of the standard kit, additional network management systems (usually a PC or host computer) with software written by the user to suit particular requirements need to be provided.

With the BT Packet NETMUX product, the in-built management and diagnostic capabilities can be extended through PSS to a Network Management Host (NMH) operating in a BT Tandem computer. User access to the NMH is via an X.28 type terminal. The NMH provides a central management database, billing and statistics records, and NUI verification. In addition to the collection of NETMUX alarm messages the NMH provides active polling of the equipment to check that it is operating correctly.

Support for Non-X.25 Non-Asynchronous Terminals

Earlier we identified several categories of non-packet mode terminals in addition to asynchronous start/stop character terminals. These were:

— terminals and workstations operating in a point-to-point block mode such as RJE;

— semi-intelligent devices operating in a block mode polled environment such as IBM 3270;

— specialised devices such as viewdata and word processors.

PSS was developed to follow the recommendations of the CCITT. Thus it has only provided support for packet-mode DTEs and asynchronous start/stop character terminals for which protocols have been well established and accepted internationally.

An essential difference between a public and private network is the range of services the network has to provide. On public networks this is generally limited to X.25 and X.3/X.28/X.29.

A private network based on X.25 is often implemented as part of the strategy towards OSI, and new terminals and systems will conform to these standards. However, that network will almost always be introduced where there is a large existing equipment base with non-OSI communication protocols; the network has to provide the appropriate interfaces to support these protocols.

Some PTTs have implemented public packet switched network PADs for which there are no CCITT recommendations. For example, GTE Telenet attaches binary synchronous communication (BSC) devices to PADs for communications with X.25 DTEs, and in Germany the Datex-P network provides PAD support for 3270 devices.

In Canada, the 3303 end-to-end protocol was developed by Bell for use on their Datapac network to support 3270 devices communicating via an X.25 network. It permits polling across a packet network and is intended to utilise this technique in conjunction with Burroughs Poll/Select as well as IBM 3270 BSC.

In the UK, the Post Office and subsequently BT, like many other PTTs, has stuck rigidly to the policy of adhering strictly to CCITT recommendations in its implementation of network PADs. Consequently users who wished to implement configurations with existing non-X.25 synchronous devices across PSS have had to provide their own non-standard PAD solutions.

Typically a non-standard private PAD will provide support for asynchronous devices, IBM 3270 and IBM 2780/3780 or HASP and telex terminals. Within large private networks these PAD facilities are often combined with X.25 concentration and switching functions provided by the communications processors supplied for packet switching.

Therefore, at the time of writing, users of PSS are only provided with PAD support for asynchronous start/stop character terminals and must resort to private PAD provision to support other non-X.25 devices. However, BT has already stated its decision to enhance PSS to support a wider range of access methods to match more closely the requirements of the broad spectrum of computers and terminals. This decision has been taken in accordance with BT's strategy of supporting Open Systems Interconnection Standards.

The enhancements to PSS will be implemented within BT's existing public data network commitment to CCITT recommendations. Aimed at offering a range of new low-cost methods to the service, the initial offerings under the new MultiStream banner, which became available from Spring 1985, include VPAD. MultiStream VPAD (described in Chapter 5) offers dial-up videotex access and is designed to accept standard viewdata terminals.

Further MultiStream access services will become available, including support for 3270 terminals and Teletex terminals. PSS is therefore destined to take on a new look as more and more MultiStream services are made available to support more and more of the non-packet mode terminals identified earlier.

No doubt the availability of such services will give rise to further protocol conversion issues apart from those applicable to access via asynchronous terminals and which have been discussed in some detail in this chapter. Such issues obviously await the launch of the service; in the meantime the following comments are included which refer to existing support for non-OSI protocols.

PAD Support for Block Mode Terminals

The CCITT have not defined any recommendations dealing with block mode type terminals. However, most network suppliers as mentioned earlier provide suitable PADs. For example, a typical block mode terminal 2780 PAD will support IBM and 'look alike' devices of the following types:

—   IBM 2780, 3780, IBM 360/370 and any other devices operating in
      contention mode.

The PAD provides a control mechanism for an X.25 based network which transfers data from terminal to host, or terminal to terminal. The data block is sent as data packets with the Q bit set to '0' and in Qualified Data packets with Q = '1' (see Chapter 7).

The PAD accepts data blocks from the terminal and assembles/ disassembles data blocks into packets for transmission as virtual calls across the network. Parameters are used at call set-up time in a similar manner to the asynchronous terminal PAD.

A block mode terminal PAD is required at each end of the network. Each PAD follows BSC link access procedures for the particular devices for link establishment, idling sequences, positive and negative acknow- ledgements, link flow control and link disconnect.

PAD Support for Polled Devices

A common feature of non-OSI protocols is that they are designed for multi-drop applications with the computer acting as the primary station and regulating communications with each drop (secondary) on the line.

The problems associated with supporting polled devices over a packet network increase beyond those encountered by more simple point-to- point devices.

Early solutions conveyed all data, including polling, across the network but this approach was soon considered inefficient, particularly as polling across networks can be expensive where the network is operated by a PTT. Other problems were also experienced through variable network delays causing frequent timeouts in the host.

If packets were only to carry polls across the network without transfer- ring data then the method is clearly not cost effective. The alternative was to develop a PAD which did not transfer polling across the network but provided local emulation at the host and terminal ends of the connection. With this approach, the asymmetric characteristics of non-OSI protocols results in two types of network interfaces; the computer to network (labelled as the PPAD) and the network to terminal (labelled as the TPAD).

Developments have lead to the concepts of Network Virtual Terminal (NVT) and Network Virtual Computer (NVC) in the PPAD and TPAD respectively, with a transport protocol between the PPAD and the TPAD to allow sessions to be opened and closed and to pass data.

The concept is based upon the host-end PAD appearing to the host as a terminal and the terminal-end PAD appearing to the terminal as a host. Thus the host polls the front-end PAD which responds to the host as if it were a terminal, but does not pass the poll to the network. Meanwhile the remote PAD polls the attached terminal as if it were the host. The PAD has to provide two functions: handling of the communications protocol, and providing those transport, session and usually presentation services required for terminal to computer communications.

For SNA devices, IBM X.25 product support includes the Network Interface Adaptor which is an external protocol converter and the X.25 program product that operates in the 3705 Communications Controller in conjunction with the Network Control Program (NCP). Several different types of packet-switched communication are described for the IBM products. One configuration uses the NPSI program product in conjunction with the NIA. In a second configuration for SNA host-to-SNA peripheral node communication, another version of the NIA replaces the NPSI program product (see Appendix 7).

Here the NIA is known as a front-end NIA and can communicate through the network to a remote NIA. Both NIAs function as an SDLC/X.25 protocol.

In order to avoid sending an excessive number of non-data packets through the network, the host polls the front-end NIA which responds to the host but does not pass the poll to the network. The remote NIA contains enough intelligence to poll its local terminals.

A further generalised capability to support IBM SNA across a packet network is provided by the ANSI draft standard which was developed jointly by IBM and Telenet in the USA.

For non-SNA devices such as the binary synchronous IBM 3270 display and the IBM 2780 remote job entry system, support is either provided within the network PAD or by a private communications processor such as that referred to earlier.

Currently a de facto standard, the Data Support Protocol (DSP), exists to provide this capability. This is an agreed standard between

Telenet, Datapac and Transpac to allow primarily IBM 3270 terminals to communicate effectively across an X.25 network.

Implementation of terminal protocols such as the IBM 3270 requires the use of at least two such devices to obtain transparency: one to emulate the host computer/TCU function and the other to emulate the IBM 3270 control unit function.

Software packages are available for the IBM 3705 front-end processor which convert BSC frames into X.25 packages destined for the terminal-end PAD associated with the control unit. Conversely X.25 packets from the PAD are converted to BSC frames within the 3705. This removes the requirement for a host-end PAD as the 'end-to-end' protocol would be contained within the 3705 software. Software packages are also available for the communications processor to provide transparent X.25 network access for both the IBM host computer system and the 3270 display system. Support for SNA host to non-standard PAD devices as identified above is provided in the NPSI program product (see Appendix 7).

Although this technique essentially provides transparent X.25 network access to the end-user, there is a measurable decrease in network performance. Typically, delays of up to two seconds, in addition to the host CPU response time, can occur just in the exchange of a simple message between a remote end-user and the host application.

Also transmitting 3270 data streams over an X.25 network is a grossly inefficient way of using such a network. The normal 3270 screen contains 2000 characters, all of which can be transmitted simultaneously under SNA/SDLC protocol operation. In PSS, and many other X.25 networks, packets are normally capable of holding 128 bytes of user data, so a considerable overhead is incurred in breaking down a 2000 character data stream into multiple 128-byte packets.

A result of this situation is the under-utilisation and incorrect utilisation of X.25 networks. Ideally the longer-term solution would be for X.25 to be brought fully into the IBM environment with device support fully integrated with the mainframe applications such as TSO and IMS. An equally flexible solution is required at each node of the network, where X.25 and SNA co-exist as a means of communication.

PAD Support for Specialised Devices

Viewdata terminals are normally supported over dialled PSTN connections into Prestel. There are, however, a number of private viewdata systems in use which are supported by packet switched networks.

To enable the private viewdata networks to access each other and Prestel, BT introduced the Prestel Gateway facility. The 'Gateway' as shown in Figure 9.8 is an X.25 connection established via PSS between a Prestel computer and a private viewdata computer.

Users of private viewdata systems normally access their database via a telephone call into a Prestel Gateway which then routes them to their own remote database via PSS (see Figure 9.8(a)).

An alternative option is to connect the terminal into a private packet network via a local PAD device. This could either be a modified asynchronous teletype PAD or a more sophisticated device which also contains the Prestel Gateway software procedures. The latter solution shown in Figure 9.8(b) is more attractive as it would allow private systems to be accessed directly and independently of Prestel but still allow access to the Prestel database as required.

For organisations without the resources of a private packet switched network the recently announced MultiStream VPAD service (see Chapter 5) will provide an alternative means of dial-up videotex access using PSS.

Word processors which have varying standards, both in communications and facilities, were not primarily designed for packet switching. In practice most word processors with communications facilities are able to send text to each other for printing at the remote end. The simplest form of word processors communicate using simple asynchronous teletype protocols whereas the more sophisticated use IBM batch protocols such as 2780. Both types can be supported on packet switched networks via the types of PADs described earlier.

Restrictions with communicating word processors means that unless they are of the same manufacture then they will only be able to transmit text for printing, not for file storage, etc. This situation arises mainly from the lack of conformity to standards. However, international telecommunications standards have been agreed for Teletex the new high-speed text communications service.

In the UK, Teletex makes use of both the PSTN and PSS. PSTN terminals will normally be connected to the network by a dedicated line.

(a)

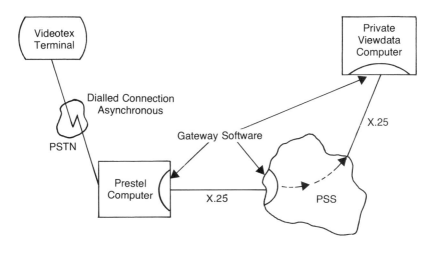

(b)

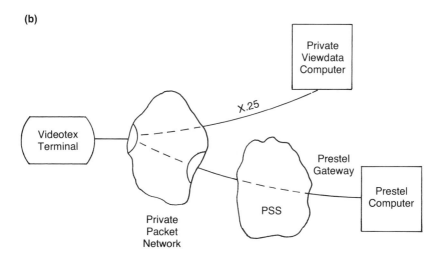

Figure 9.8 Prestel Gateway

Some Teletex devices will allow the connection of more than one exchange line and may support a number of terminals. Teletex messages sent on the PSTN will normally be transmitted at 2400 bps. PSS terminals will be connected by a dataline and will operate at one of the available synchronous speeds (2.4, 9.6, 48 Kbits/s). Output at the appropriate speed for the receiving terminal is assured by the network.

A Teletex terminal can be one of many types including simple memory typewriters, word processors, or sophisticated computer systems. The connection from terminal equipment into the Teletex network will be via an equipment interface conforming to CCITT standards and as such will allow a full interconnection ability for all terminal equipment meeting such recommendations.

Although a few Teletex terminals are individually equipped for packet-mode operation, the majority of users cannot justify a permanent dataline connection. Individual terminals tend to be connected over dial-up circuits with permanent connections to PSS used mainly for terminal cluster controllers. Interworking between PSTN and PSS is accomplished using the InterStream Two gateway (see Chapter 6). This enables messages to be sent between a Teletex terminal on the PSS and a Teletex terminal on the PSTN.

InterStream Three provides a conversion facility which allows the transfer of messages between the Teletex services on either PSTN or PSS, and the Telex network.

A major advantage of the new services is that communications between devices of different speeds will be achieved. In this way, a word processor transmitting at say 2400 bps is able to link with a telex machine operating at only 50 bps, the buffering facilities being provided at the local Teletex exchange.

A protocol conversion necessary to enable devices to talk to each other is also provided by the exchange.

Support for a much wider range of terminals will be provided by the proposed MultiStream Teletex access service when this becomes available from BT (see Chapter 5).

10 The Role of PSS

INTRODUCTION

The previous chapters have described the PSS service and associated X.25 products and network arrangements. This chapter reviews the role of PSS. The remaining chapters examine the various applications.

The unique features of packet switching are identified; their significance is discussed; and the historical arguments which are advanced in defining its role in relation to the alternative services are then summarised.

The direct test of any new product or service is its reception in the marketplace. PSS has only been operational for a few years. Thus there has only been a relatively brief period in which users have been able to assimilate and evaluate any benefits which can result from use of the service. Nevertheless, there is today a growing user base with considerable experience which warrants further examination.

Since the introduction to PSS in *Why Packet Switching?* (1982), the NCC has frequently monitored this type of experience by conducting surveys and research amongst its members and associated organisations. More recently, a short series of interviews was carried out with organisations who could be identified as active users of the PSS service. The results and conclusions which emerge from these visits to a wide cross-section of industry and commerce are combined with the results of previous surveys of user experience of PSS and presented in the subsequent chapters.

In these chapters following a look at a number of applications of PSS in various fields of industry and commerce, the main opportunities which

153

are presented by the service on the basis of the current evidence are summarised.

It is hoped that this concluding section of the book will provide some guidance which will assist users by pointing them in the right direction and which will focus their attention on those situations and application characteristics which they should look for when evaluating the service. To develop this aspect further these chapters examine some of the major applications of PSS and draw upon case studies for further illustrations.

FEATURES OF PUBLIC PACKET SWITCHED NETWORKS

In the earlier chapters the various features of packet switching services have been described. The most salient of these features are listed below:

— switched service;

— variable network propagation delay;

— provides for standardised X.25 call multiplexing;

— improved error performance;

— simpler physical host computer interface;

— functionally complex X.25 interface;

— speed matching and terminal matching capability;

— low level protocol conversion;

— centralised network management support;

— high integrity;

— ease of network reconfiguration;

— distance independent access;

— traffic dominated usage charge.

WHY USE PSS? (The Role of PSS)

General

There has been much speculation about the role of PSS in the market-place, and the benefits it can offer compared with the alternative services. In this context, the broad conclusions which have historically emerged are based largely upon the features which have been described in the earlier chapters and in particular on the unique tariff structures of PSS.

The total cost of using a service can be specified in terms of a selection of variables and parameters which between them describe the particular properties of the service, the facilities which are used, and the extent of the usage. The usage of a service will be strongly influenced by the amount of traffic and traffic patterns. For example it may be appropriate to describe the traffic as that of high volume, long duration, or 'bursty' (short duration traffic).

Depending upon the particular service and its associated tariff structure, some particular collection of parameters will be significant. Parameters which directly affect costs will be represented amongst the cost components of the relevant tariff structure.

A user of the X.25 public data network such as PSS is faced with a rather more complex tariff structure than that for the more traditional circuit switched and leased line services. Leased circuit charges are based upon the length and speed of the circuit and are totally irrespective of the amount of traffic which is being transferred and the time taken for the transfer of the traffic. Circuit switching relates to a usage charge which is dependent upon the total connect time and the distance involved in the individual call. For a specific service the usage charge would typically be obtained from the distance tables for a given type of leased circuit, or the staged tariff for a dial-up connection. With PSS, however, the usage charge is predominantly related to the volume of traffic which is transmitted and (to a lesser extent) to the duration of the call.

In order to determine which is the most attractive service for a particular application a careful analysis of all costs must be completed.

Simple quantitative models and rule-of-thumb approaches have been used for some time in comparing the costs of traditional services.

Cost Analysis

A commonly used technique relies upon the expression of tariff costs over a range of traffic volumes as illustrated in Figure 10.1. This approach makes certain assumptions such as distance/speed combinations for leased circuits, distance of circuit switched call and call connect times for both circuit switched and PSS calls. Nevertheless, this rule-of-thumb approach enables a comparison of the costs of the three services to be made. This illustrates that packet switching is most attractive for applications with a low- to mid-range traffic volume; whereas for high volumes, leased circuits are the most cost effective, and for a few short transactions each day, circuit switched facilities become most attractive.

Although this technique enables useful conclusions to be drawn for a given set of circumstances, its value would be enhanced by relating traffic volumes to specific users' traffic and application needs, and by evaluating the sensitivity of tariff costs to changes in parameter values.

Bleazard in *Evaluating Data Transmission Services* (1983) describes a more sophisticated approach which enables these types of investigations to be pursued. In this method the basis for comparison is to express costs in terms of bits per month. The costs of alternative services are represented as functions of service parameters which are then plotted graphically.

The following is the set of service parameters which are utilised:

—   line speed;

—   distance;

—   call density;

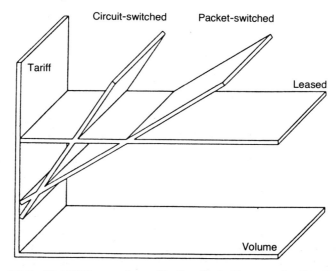

Figure 10.1   Tariff Parameters affecting Data Communication Services

— traffic volume;

— block/packet length;

— call duration;

— communication intensity.

The total cost is divided into two components: an access charge and a usage charge. For the main categories of service, the access charge depends primarily on the speed of the circuit or the access channel.

The second component of the equation depends upon the amount of service usage. Table 10.1 lists for each service category the relevant parameters which enter into the usage charge.

Service Category	Parameters
Leased Circuits	circuit length line speed
Circuit switched	call duration time distance
Packet Switched	traffic volume (packets) call duration

Table 10.1   Usage Charge Parameters

The usage cost is represented by an expression describing the uses charge for the specific service.

Additional tariff features may be present, and may include, for example, a call set-up charge or a high traffic volume discount.

The addition of the access and the usage terms provides the total cost side of the equation which by applying simple factors is converted to a monthly cost/bit basis.

In addition to the five parameters traffic volume, line speed, call density, distance, and call duration, there are two others which are given special mention in this approach. The block or packet length is regarded as particularly relevant because both the period and the extent to which the full capacity is utilised have an important bearing on the utilisation of the line. The remaining parameter, which is the communications intensity, is regarded as particularly relevant within the packet switching context and the move towards traffic dependent tariff structures. This parameter measures the extent to which the communications channel capacity is utilised and provides a more precise way of describing traffic patterns and distinguishing between degrees of 'burstyness'.

To complete the model a subset of parameters which describe or reflect the application characteristics are chosen. For illustrative purposes four categories of applications were selected, these are remote job entry (or file transfer), scientific, enquiry response, and business (transaction orientated).

Summary of Results of Cost Analysis

The main conclusions of the investigation insofar as they apply to the tariff structures, tariff relativities and profile parameters assumed in the study are:

— leased line services are advantageous at high traffic volumes, especially if the communications intensity is also high;

— for switched services, packet switching is economic for low to moderate traffic volumes and low communications intensity. As the volume increases, however, together with increasing communications intensity and line speed, circuit switching becomes more advantageous.

Figure 10.2 restates these results in a qualitative fashion; it shows the three service regions defined in terms of traffic volume and communications intensity. Thus for high volumes, private circuits are favoured, other things being equal, and in deciding between PSS and circuit switched services, low communications intensities favour PSS. In other words, the tariff structure of PSS favours applications which have a bursty traffic characteristic and a low communications intensity.

Benefits of PSS

PSS is particularly suited to those applications with the following characteristics:

— bursty traffic;

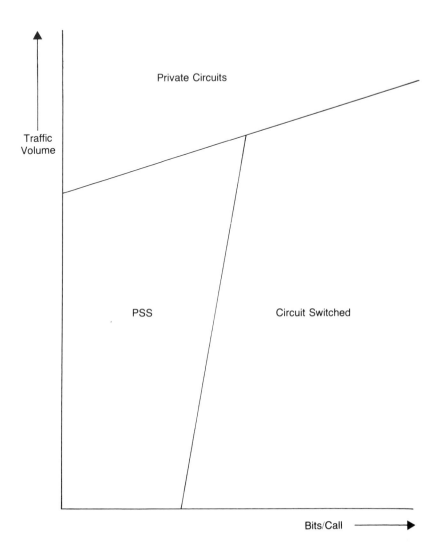

Figure 10.2   Economic Region for Private Circuits, PSS and Circuit Switched Services

— low communications intensity;

— widely dispersed or disparate terminals;

— multiple remote host or applications accessed by a single local access circuit terminal and circuit;

— access to international packet switched services.

Cost saving opportunities arise from the unique PSS tariff structure which is totally independent of distance but related to actual traffic volumes and as such favours low traffic intensity calls. Other cost savings arise from the connection and interfacing arrangements of X.25, X.3, X.28 and X.29, such as:

— standardised multiplexing;

— single line local access which leads to a reduction in point-to-point circuit costs;

— increased freedom of choice of terminals which alleviates multiple terminal provision.

Further savings can result from:

— ease of reconfiguration and attachment of new devices;

— network management facilities including standby provision.

Chief opportunities for cost reductions at a mainframe site lie in reduced local line interface costs (and modem costs) together with a reduction in network management costs. The X.25 interface provides opportunities for simplifying the line interface particularly for dial-up lines. All dial-up traffic to PSS, instead of being presented at the customer mainframe site as distinct low-speed circuits, is concentrated onto a far smaller number of higher speed synchronous circuits. Apart from simplifying the physical distribution and access arrangements, there will be a corresponding reduction in modem and computer port requirements. Furthermore, through the adoption of X.25 the interface is also standardised, thus increasing the interconnection potential of the network.

For a sizeable terminal population and associated mainframe line terminations, these cost savings may be quite significant. However, the price that has to be paid for the above advantages is a greater functional complexity in the interface. This requires substantial intelligence and as such may possibly require major modifications to the mainframe computer systems software. This would particularly apply to suppliers' older product ranges.

Network management facilities are being increasingly regarded as a major benefit of PSS. For PSTN access they provide a facility which is not currently available and for some point-to-point and multipoint private circuit configurations they could possibly swing the balance towards PSS for those organisations who wish to minimise their network management overheads. Multipoint circuits in particular have always presented special problems for network management and fault diagnosis. The potential value of PSS network management support which is inherent in the service should therefore not be ignored and should be included in any evaluation of the service.

Finally, with BT committed to packet switching as a major 'Open Systems' service which complements the advances in digital circuit switching and digital private circuits, and with the growth of applications which involve inter-organisational data communications, the opportunities of OSI and the adoption of X.25 has great strategic significance for interworking opportunities. It also provides access to those value-added services for which packet switching may be either the most economic or even a mandatory form of access.

As the core X.25 network, PSS alone cannot meet all the cost/performance requirements of the marketplace. The introduction of the local distribution network (MultiStream) enhances the basic PSS service to provide more flexible and effective support for smaller hosts and terminals. Further enhancements result from links to other networks through the InterStream gateways.

The Wider View

PSS offers some significant cost saving opportunities when it is regarded purely as a direct substitute for the traditional PSTN and leased line services. However, an evaluation which is based only upon cost-saving criteria takes a far too narrow a view of the potential benefits and also of how the role of PSS might develop in the medium and long term. A much more broadly based assessment should give great weight to the unique features of PSS, and to the new business and application opportunities which it may present. How the role of PSS is likely to evolve must obviously be considered within the context of both the existing traditional services which have been referred to earlier and the newly emerging digital services such as KiloStream and ISDN.

KiloStream is enabling BT to gradually replace analogue Datel private circuits by digital private circuits and as such is being offered at extremely competitive cost terms compared with analogue circuits with modems. This is attractive at all data rates and over all but the shortest distances, and is substantially cheaper at the higher data rates than the specially provided wideband circuits.

Within the present pilot ISDN service the use of digital access is seen as providing cost and operational advantages over the use of modems and analogue plant, especially at the higher data rates (Dataline 48K). In the longer term, although it is possible that PSS may ultimately converge with ISDN, the need for offering X.25 packet switched data communications to ISDN users is expected to continue, even after extensive introduction of circuit switched ISDN services. This is due to the particular advantages of packet switching for interactive applications (ie bursty traffic) and the multi-channel access features of X.25.

Therefore a complete and comprehensive evaluation of PSS needs to look far beyond the immediate short-term cost savings goals and consider how the unique features of PSS can be exploited to support new applications and perhaps open up new commercial opportunities which in themselves might not otherwise be cost effective using either the traditional services or other alternatives.

PSS has been with us now for around six years as a commercial operation. In the following chapters, we shall look at some of the ways in which organisations have utilised the service. From this, conclusions can be drawn which provide some guidance for users by pointing them in the right direction and by focusing their attention on those situations and applications which they should look for when evaluating the service.

11 Applications for PSS

INTRODUCTION

When the PSS Service was launched in 1981, it was intended to complement other public Data Communication Services rather than be suitable for all types of applications. PSS and Packet Switching are particularly suited to the interactive type of application in which traffic is sent in bursts with relatively long intervals of silence in between the bursts. Applications which envisage this type of usage were time-sharing bureaux, on-line database access, and on-line credit card checking. It was also considered that PSS would prove attractive for distributed computing, especially for linking together different computer systems into a composite computer network. PSS was less likely to be suitable for applications which involved only remote batch data transmission: for example, RJE and batched data entry.

Today the number of customers and the volume of calls within the UK and to other countries on PSS is doubling each year. The predominant applications for PSS have included information retrieval from computer databases within the UK and overseas, credit card validation, and automatic clearance of bank payments between clearing houses (CHAPS). Other major applications have included: the inventory control and customs clearance of air freight by the major airlines through the UK airports; and use as a Prestel Gateway facility.

Growth in the use of PSS is expected to continue at a high rate as the service becomes more available to users in the UK and broadens its capability to take on new applications such as value-added network services, with the increase in network capacity and service enhancements such as MultiStream and InterStream. Future uses of PSS are likely to include electronic funds transfer at the point of sale (EFTPOS) and other industry related networks, together with new forms of electronic mail and other message services; in particular, Teletex.

International PSS (IPSS) is becoming more and more attractive to the multinational organisations for access to corporate business management information and software development facilities throughout the world. In particular, IPSS provides access to over 56 public data networks in more than 40 countries of the world; this means that over 90% of the developed world, including the major trading countries, can be accessed through PSS.

In this chapter we look briefly at three of the predominant but special-ised applications of PSS; ie credit card authorisation services, automatic clearance of bank payments between clearing houses (CHAPS), and public electronic mail services (Telecom Gold). After briefly describing these types of applications, to which packet switching is particularly suited, in later chapters we look in greater detail at applications of PSS which are perhaps of more general interest to organisations involved in the business of planning and operating commercial data communication services. Today three of the most significant areas which are emerging in this field are:

— on-line information retrieval services;

— valued-added network services;

— international networking.

To illustrate the use of PSS in each of these areas, the subsequent chapters include a fairly detailed description of several case studies based upon users' experience in the UK.

CREDIT CARD AUTHORISATION SYSTEM

Requirements

Today many people in the UK purchase goods by credit card. Alongside this, the fraudulent usage of credit cards is currently costing the banks several million pounds a year.

To counter fraudulent use, it is usual for stores, garages, hotels, etc to make customary credit card checks by telephoning the credit card com-pany. This method is both costly (in terms of distance of telephone call), and far from foolproof, because it is based on sample checks only.

What was required was a fast, cheap, error-free method facilitating complete checks on all credit cards, in essence an ability to be 'on-line' to credit card companies' computers, whether in the UK or abroad, via one transaction terminal, and where the overhead cost per transaction made the method cost effective.

In order to satisfy this need, a study was made of the facilities and costs of the alternative data transmission techniques available. These are:

— Dial-up;

— Private Circuits;

— PSS.

Why PSS?

As a result of the study, PSS was adopted on the grounds of:

— low cost per transaction;

— high data transmission reliability;

— flexibility;

— data network control facilities;

— ease of expansion of network;

— ability and cost effectiveness for overseas connection.

In particular, reliability of data transmission – which guarantees security of data through use of X.25 and triple X (X.3, X.28, X.29) protocols – was seen as a significant benefit of PSS for this application.

Flexibility was considered a key factor based on two particular aspects of PSS. The first is the facilities of the public data network itself: subscribers, at local call rate, are provided with access across the whole network both throughout the UK, and onward to international public data networks. Secondly, the protocols used in packet-switching techniques enable a varied number of transaction terminal types to access an equally varied number of computers. In the case of small retailers this is particularly attractive in keeping initial connection costs to a minimum, and, as and when required, providing additional connection to other credit card company computers at no additional terminal or network connection charge.

Further significant features were the provision of network control facilities and ease of expansion of the network. PSS, being a public data network, provided subscribers with complete network control, whereas a private circuit network would have required the provision of individual network control facilities, with the overhead of additional costs.

Where a subscriber needs to expand his point-of-sale terminal population he has the choice of terminal types, and location, at no increase in connection costs. The network also provides for wider database access; and increased point-of-sale facilities; ie direct debiting could be adopted simply and at minimal cost.

Implementation

Transaction telephones are currently being installed in a wide number of retail outlets in the UK.

Transaction telephones are basically terminals capable of functioning either as a telephone, carrying voice traffic and providing all the facilities of the modern telephone, or as data terminals transmitting data over the PSS network. Although being marketed as a first step toward the automation of both credit and debit payments of all kinds, for the present, transaction telephones only involve credit authorisation for the four major credit card companies (Barclaycard, Amex, Access and Diners) and some in-house credit cards.

The terminals are designed to read cards with ISO Track 2 magnetic stripes which contain information on the Credit Card Issuer, the customer's account number and the card expiry date. By wiping the card through the terminal and keying in the amount of the sale on the keyboard, the operator automatically triggers off the call to the relevant host computer without having to lift the handset.

While the transmission of data is in progress, the name of the card issuer being contacted is displayed. Within 20-30 seconds, the response from the host computer is displayed. If the transaction cannot be authorised the telephone may be automatically programmed to dial a credit card supervisor. The operator is alerted to make voice contact when the call is established.

In addition to authorising credit, the terminals allow retailers to offer their customers the facility to raise cash against their credit cards by following the authorisation procedure in the normal way. Later they will also probably be used to check the validity of cheque guarantee cards since these have ISO Track 2 magnetic stripes which can be wiped in the same way as credit cards.

Installation is a relatively simple process. All that is required is a standard British Telecom telephone point and 13 amp mains outlet. The terminals when they first arrive on the retailers' premises are blank and have to be 'initialised' with basic information, such as the contact numbers for the host credit card computers. This process of 'initialisation' is carried out by either wiping through cards containing the data, or by downloading it from a central computer at BT. Each terminal is allocated a unique identity number by BT. After initialisation the terminals are ready for use.

The BT Credit Authorisation Service provides communications via the PSS network with regionally sited network multiplexers directing and controlling the calls to the card issuers. The service consists of the specialised telephones (including modems, local intelligence, card wipe and display), and the telephone access network to custom-programmed PADs which interface to PSS and thus the card issuer's computer as shown in Figure 11.1. The service uses the standard X.25 and X.3/28/29 packet switching protocols supplemented by agreed message formats for each transaction.

The protocol referred to in full as the '300 bps IBRO Transaction Tele Protocol' guarantees error control throughout the connection. As shown in Figure 11.2 both exchange line and leased line connections are provided, but in the case of leased line connections access is made to a locally-sited multiplexer such as the BT Packet NETMUX. This solution is often more cost effective in retail centres where high transaction rates can be expected or heavy customer service demands exist. For the larger multi-terminal retail centre, installation of a multiplexer in store as shown in Figure 11.3 provides direct and rapid access to PSS. It is also possible for a number of users to share a private packet multiplexer.

Summary

PSS has been established as the ideal vehicle for the retailer requiring

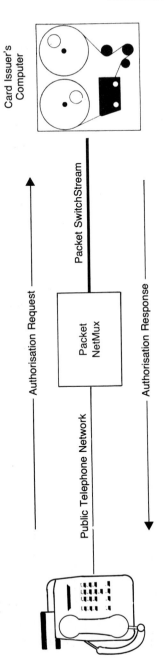

Figure 11.1

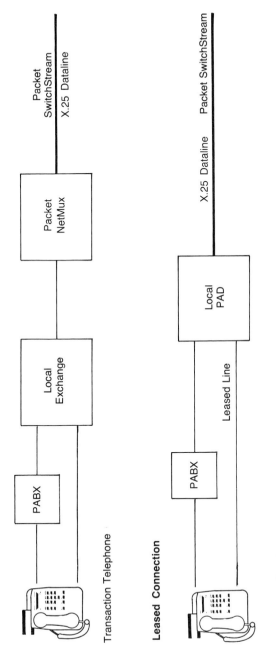

Figure 11.2

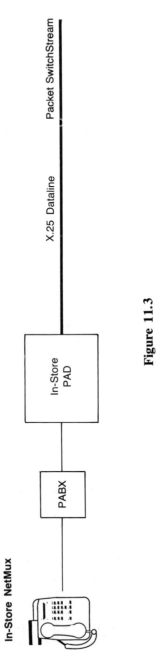

In-Store NetMux

Figure 11.3

immediate credit card authorisation with the ability to access computer databases throughout the UK and worldwide, using a mixed terminal population, with guaranteed reliability and error protection at low cost.

The transaction telephone is seen as a step towards fully automated payments, at the same time providing retailers with a valuable facility today. However, the full benefit of transaction telephones will only be realised when the transactions are made paperless. Some progress is being made in the development of an electronic funds transfer service (EFTS) network in the UK, but it seems unlikely that paperless transactions using transaction telephones will be introduced on any significant scale before 1988.

As point-of-sale activities increase, particularly through the development of electronic funds transfer service at the point-of-sale (EFTPOS), PSS is capable of meeting the expansion at minimal additional cost to the subscriber.

Building on the success of PSS with the Credit Authorisation Service and CHAPS (see next section), BT is likely to be a major contractor to the Clearing Banks and financial community for the detailed design of an EFTPOS network. This project will use PSS and MultiStream as its main networking vehicle.

CLEARING HOUSE AUTOMATED PAYMENTS SYSTEM (CHAPS)

In the UK, each of the Clearing Banks maintains a special clearing account with the Bank of England which is used at the end of each day to make payments to or from other Clearing Banks. For many years Town Clearing has provided a traditional paper clearing system but only within the boundaries of the City of London and for high-value items (currently above £10,000).

Although Town Clearing (Figure 11.4) is run smoothly and efficiently, it suffers from the limitations of a manual system, ie unwieldy operation and rising labour costs, together with the restrictions imposed by being available only within the boundaries of London, and up to close of business at 3 pm. Such drawbacks, coupled with the acceptance of electronic funds transfer worldwide, led to a decision taken by the Clearing Banks to create CHAPS (Figure 11.5), an up-to-date automated payment system for the City which would enable it to maintain its

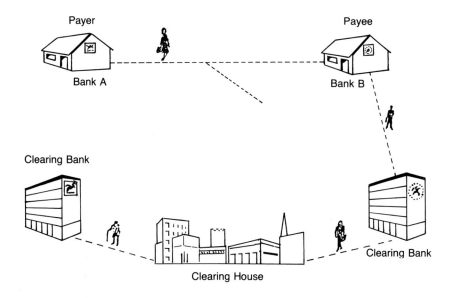

Figure 11.4   Present Paper-Based System

position as an international financial centre to the end of the century and beyond.

Requirements

After a period of study, a decision was taken to build a new purpose-built computer system to handle high-value same-day payments. In concept it was to be fairly traditional, with a large central processor and an operating organisation allowing network access to all the various potential users of the service, either via a terminal or a direct link between the user's own computer system and the CHAPS central machine.

As the development of the initial design proceeded, a number of problem areas emerged. Firstly, as there was a commitment to make the service available widely throughout the City and outside, to whoever might require it, the one system was required to support a large number of different requirements. As a result the complexity of the system, and therefore its cost, escalated rapidly.

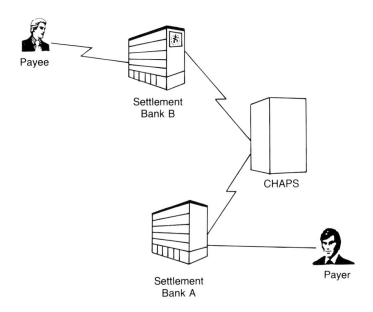

Figure 11.5 CHAPS Payment System

A second problem arose in trying to obtain the level of security necessary in a system which would deal with such enormous sums of money, while at the same time retaining the flexibility necessary to satisfy all requirements.

It became apparent that it would not be possible to maintain security of the level considered necessary without imposing unacceptable constraints on some users. The result, as well as a further increase in costs, was a drop in the projected traffic for the system and a resultant increase in the charge per transaction necessary to make provision of the service economical.

With the technical modifications and difficulties inherent in any computer development of this size and complexity, the viability of the centralised concept was questioned and a decision was made to make a clean break, and to consider a more distributed approach based on development in computer technology and in the provision of public data networks. It was felt that the system would be more successful if it had the minimum of central development and control, and allowed each Clearing Bank to deal largely independently with questions of service provision, of security and of tariff.

Although the Clearing Banks operate the core clearing systems, there is a long history of agency agreements with a wide variety of other financial institutions which allow them the access to the various clearing systems.

It was decided that this 'two tiered' structure where the Clearing Banks together operate clearing systems for other organisations, including other banks, should be perpetuated in CHAPS.

The idea was that a group of Clearing Banks would be known as CHAPS settlement banks because of their ability to settle one with another at the Bank of England, and would each provide what has come to be known as the CHAPS Gateway. These Gateways would be able to exchange payment messages via PSS, and at the same time would provide a standard interface to each bank's own payment systems. These in turn would support connections to customers. The Gateway would provide only those audit, routeing, and communications control functions necessary to ensure the orderly and secure operation of the overall service. Standard Gateway software would be used by all settlement banks.

Why PSS?

PSS was adopted because it avoided the need for the development of a jointly owned network and passed the responsibility for network control and operation from the banks to BT. This was of prime importance in complying with the fundamental principle of CHAPS which stated that there was to be no central organisation to operate CHAPS and that joint development should be minimised.

PSS also provided standards through the X.25 and triple X protocols used in packet switching which allowed ease of connection by a variety of users with differing requirements and systems. Again this minimised joint development activities.

It was also seen as providing the level of security and reliability necessary for this type of operation and, at the same time, retaining the flexibility to meet all requirements well into the future.

Finally the service was available both in the City, through the UK and worldwide to whoever might need it.

Implementation

As shown in Figure 11.6, CHAPS is a distributed system with intelligent terminals situated in each settlement bank linked through PSS. Eight 'gateways' are provided for the clearing banks either to operate for themselves or to share with a smaller clearer. Each gateway, which is based on a Tandem computer, allows the settlement banks to exchange payment messages and also permits the flexibility of message delivery by other banks and institutions by on-line or off-line connection to the settlement banks. Figure 11.7 shows a typical settlement bank gateway arrangement.

The system uses the method of credit clearing, whereby the transaction is initiated by the payer to be received by the payee as cleared funds, in other words payment will be guaranteed once a payment message has been sent. Settlement is carried out by each settlement bank sending CHAPS payment messages to the Bank of England to transfer payments between special accounts.

CHAPS is designed for major payments between organisations: for example, the corporate treasurer who wishes to ensure that company funds are not left lying idle; a bank which has been requested to make a sterling payment by a customer; a solicitor or individual completing the selling and purchase of property. In principle, anyone can ask his settlement bank to make a same-day payment provided that he has the funds and an accepted means of instructing the bank.

Having decided to carry out instructions to make a payment on a same day basis by means of a CHAPS payment, the settlement bank first carries out procedures to ensure that the payment is in order. Because each settlement bank guarantees each CHAPS payment it makes, payment authorisation is a matter only for the settlement bank and its customer. To ensure security of this process, great care has been taken in selecting the algorithm and ensuring that knowledge of the authentication process is restricted.

In addition to the encryption of every payment message passing between gateways, further security is provided by keeping secure audit trails

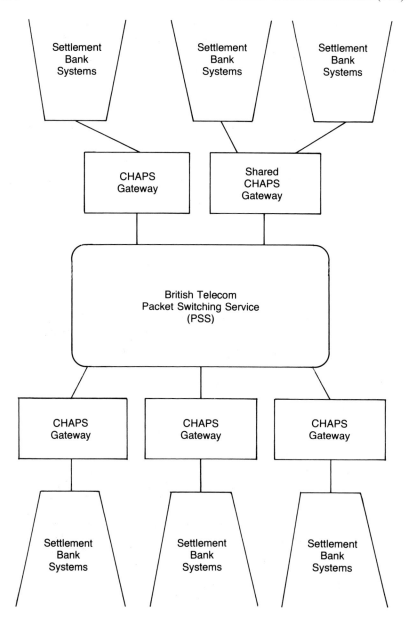

Figure 11.6   The Heart of the CHAPS System

at several stages in a message's progress through the system, by including a time-stamp and a total value sent to date in every payment message, and by an elaborate system of message numbering and procedures both between gateways, and between each settlement bank's own systems and its gateway.

At the end of the day a special network function is evoked causing final interbank totals to be computed, agreed and passed over the network to the Bank of England.

Protection against failure is achieved through the use of the Tandem 'Non-Stop' computers which are designed to continue operation even

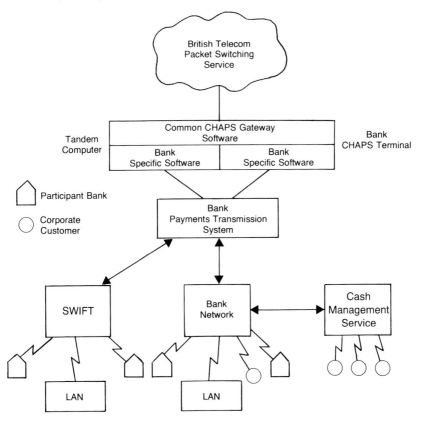

Figure 11.7

after multiple failures. Provision is also made by each settlement bank to switch to an alternative site in the event of a complete gateway failure and alternative procedures have been defined which enable service to continue even if the second gateway fails. Similar special arrangements have been made to protect against failures in the PSS network.

Summary

CHAPS is a credit transfer system but, unlike the existing Town Clearing, is automated and because it can be connected both to bank branch networks and to participant's systems, it provides a same day service over the entire country. PSS removed the responsibilities of joint network development and provided the degree of flexibility and network penetration, together with the levels of security and reliability necessary for this type of operation.

TELECOM GOLD

Telecom Gold is a new company set up by BT to market their electronic mail service called DialCom. The service was developed in the USA by ITT DialCom and uses central computers in London to provide publicly available worldwide electronic mail and information management facilities.

Access to the service is available through national and international public telephone and data networks. The electronic mail service is designed to be both easy to use and inexpensive.

A subscriber to the service is usually able to connect most of his existing terminals such as microcomputers, word processors and VDUs to the central computers by a single dial-in connection and log-on procedure. The computer provides the user with a password protected workspace which contains the electronic equivalent of office information; other people can send messages to the workspace but only the subscriber can read or alter the contents. Single commands allow the subscriber to SEND messages, READ incoming items, SCAN the 'in-tray' and DISTRIBUTE, FILE or RETRIEVE information. In addition to mail services, Telecom Gold provides information handling and storage facilities for filing, updating, data validation, data extraction, calculation and formatting.

A subscriber to the electronic mail service is also provided with direct access to several other BT services. A Telex link allows outgoing Telex messages to be sent directly to the UK and international networks (and also allows telex terminals to be used to access electronic mail). Telemessages which replaced the inland telegrams can be sent in the same way as electronic mail messages. Radiopaging enables subscribers to be alerted automatically when urgent messages arrive in their mailbox.

Using PSS

Within the UK three types of connection are offered to terminal users; dial-up, PSS, and direct. Within London direct dial-up is the preferred method within local call band areas. Outside London PSS is the recommended means of connection. Telecom Gold offers a link service facility to all PSS exchanges in the UK. By using a 'common NUI', individual subscribers are saved from registering with PSS and are presented with all data connection costs on one bill from Telecom Gold.

Subscribers with a larger terminal population at a single site can opt for a direct link to the electronic mail service. This type of connection often provides a more cost-effective service together with a higher speed of operation and faster access.

In addition to Telecom Gold a number of countries offer the DialCom electronic mail service outside the UK operated by ITT DialCom or its licencees. Once connected to his workspace a subscriber keys in an international code and address (or name if using the electronic mail directory). Apart from sending electronic mail from the UK to users in other countries, subscribers travelling abroad can access Telecom Gold over international public telephone or data networks. For regular travel the cost of dialling direct can be cut by subscribing to local national public data networks and accessing Telecom Gold through IPSS/PSS.

Implementation

The central computer system shown in Figure 11.8 comprises several host computers (PRIME) interconnected through an X.25 switched network. This provides a gateway to the PSS, PSTN and leased line connections and routes incoming calls directly to user suites in each of the hosts. A terminal PAD arrangement is provided for dial-up connections, and sub-addressing is used within the X.25 calls to direct them to the appropriate host. Two Dataline 9600 connections are currently installed to handle the volume of traffic with the PSS Multi-line facility selected

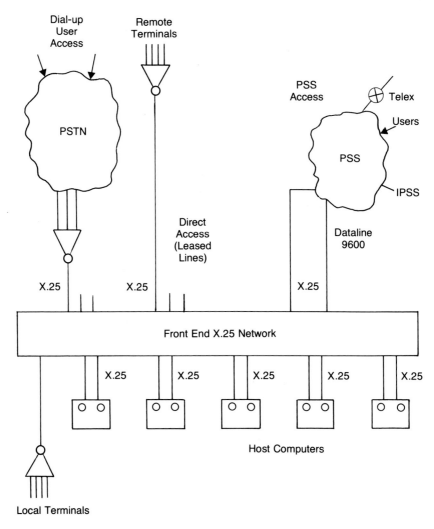

Figure 11.8   Telecom Gold Network

to allow both datalines to have the same network user address (NUA).

Summary

PSS is primarily seen as a terminal capture network, providing relatively low cost and error-free connections (compared with dial-up) for UK subscribers located outside London, and via IPSS for subscribers outside the UK. It also avoided the need for development of a private networking infrastructure and its associated network control and operational functions and responsibilities.

IPSS/PSS is also considered attractive for sending mail to other hosts in other countries where traffic demands are light. For busier routes, such as the North America link, private circuits are considered more cost effective. In all cases mail is batched up and transported at specified times using a 'mail bag' concept.

The PSS/Telex gateway (InterStream One) described in Chapter 6 has also provided an alternative means of access to electronic mail services for users who only have telex terminals; this is considered a significant advantage for subscribers in many of the third world countries where Telex is predominantly used.

12 PSS in On-Line Information Services

INTRODUCTION

On-line Information Services have always been heavy users of packet switching in the US, and over the last few years European countries have found packet switching to be the most convenient and most cost-effective means of access to many of the world's database services. In Europe this has been advanced by the coming into service of the European networks and international PSS. This application is a rapidly expanding area because of the tremendous interest and enthusiasm of the more advanced organisations in their search for information and knowledge which today has been made available to people in all walks of life through the advent of low-cost micro technology.

SCENARIO

One of the most significant and growing uses of PSS in the UK is a means of access to public databases by on-line information retrieval.

On-line retrieval (Figure 12.1) is access to a computer using a simple keyboard terminal connected either by a permanent circuit or, more commonly, by a dial-up telephone line. The development of information retrieval is fairly recent and its growth has depended on the availability of facilities for public data communications and on the construction of sophisticated software programs by the information vendors.

Although computerised databases have been available for many years, until the 1970s most could only be searched in batch mode.

On-line searching offers a number of advantages: for example, the enquirer retains direct communications with the computer and interrogates it in real-time; the answers can be obtained immediately from the information services.

With the advent of international public data networks such as Telenet, Datapac, Euronet, DDX-P, and Austpac it has now become possible for a user with a simple terminal to dial into computers in the US, Canada, Europe, Japan, and even Australia as well as within the UK. Whatever the location it is possible to achieve accurate and error-free data transfer

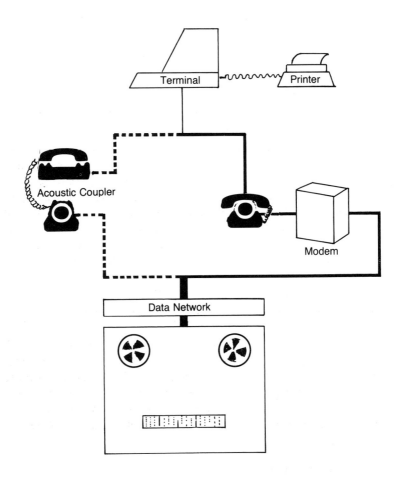

Figure 12.1   On-line Information Retrieval

at a relatively low cost. It is no longer necessary to suffer the delays of the international and national postal service; nor does it matter where the information database is located.

At the time of writing, there were over 1800 on-line databases available covering a spectrum of scientific, technical, business, social sciences and humanities. Examples of such databases include:

— addresses and data on the top 20,000 UK companies;

— details of over 7,000 trade opportunities and business contacts worldwide;

— 4 million references on biological subjects;

— daily time series on prices of major commodities and currency exchange rates;

— over 300 million words of law including UK law reports, legislation, taxation, and employment/industrial relations law.

Database directories are available to guide prospective users to suitable databases and to provide information on the database provider and host supplier. In a minority of cases, the database is made available to the user directly by the database provider. It is more common, however, for the provider to sell the database to an organisation which runs the host computer and subsequently sells access to the database to the user. Most hosts will purchase a range of databases, typically 10-50, covering both specialised and general subject areas. A single contract placed with the host provides the user with access to all or most of the databases being offered. Charges are made by the host for use of a database. These usually comprise a charge for the length of time connected to the database, together with a charge for the amount of data retrieved.

In the UK, the On-Line Information Centre, set up in 1979 with support from Government to promote the effective use of on-line databases, provides a database enquiry service for subscribers. The Centre holds a collection of database directories, provides information on many of the databases and hosts, and offers advice on the choice of databases and hosts, and on problems relating to the setting up and running of a search service.

A QUESTION OF ACCESS

In on-line information searching it is the host organisation which has the powerful and sophisticated processing capability necessary for searching large databases. At the user end all that is required is a relatively simple and inexpensive terminal. The choice is extremely wide and many organisations may already possess the necessary equipment. This may include a computer terminal with a small low cost printer or a simple printer and keyboard.

A suitable terminal can cost from £400 upwards if purchased outright. Leasing a terminal for about £50 to £200 per month provides an option which enables the choice to be fully checked against specific requirements.

Today, an option which is becoming very popular is the use of a low-cost microcomputer equipped with a printer which can also be used for local computing tasks and word processing as well as on-line communications. Using this equipment can often lead to a doubling on investment by increasing utilisation without further expenditure apart from a small charge for extra software.

But the major attractions with on-line information retrieval are the facilities for editing and modifying search results or the downloading or transferring of results to a magnetic storage media for further editing off-line.

With most micros it is usually necessary to acquire a 'communications' or 'intelligent terminal' software package or chip which makes them compatible with the database or databases to which they are connected. No single package will be compatible with all micros because of differences in operating systems; it is therefore important to check that the package being offered is available for the particular type of micro and particular type of configuration being used.

A software package usually labelled Teletype or Asynchronous is required to enable the micro to talk over PSS to the host computer. It is the emulation feature of the package which is essential for this type of terminal. A wide variety of packages for microcomputers costing just over £100 are now available on the market; particular features which may be required include:

—   dial-up

An auto-dial facility is useful particularly if it is possible to list a directory of auto-dial numbers, to change numbers easily and to link particular numbers with certain communications parameters required by a host.

— duplex parity and speed selection

This feature would allow the terminal to be switched to a different duplex mode or a different transmission speed and in so doing would allow access to a variety of host computers as well as choice of modem or acoustic coupler.

— error handling

The software should allow continuous communications despite minor errors but at the same time should be able to abort commands if an error is a serious one and, more importantly perhaps, communicate the fact that an error has been detected to the user by giving a meaningful error message.

— data capture

It is often useful to store data which has been found on the on-line information system onto a disk in the micro, for editing or for merging with existing files already in use. A facility which allows the capture of data and down loading onto the disk is a very useful feature particularly if it allows the manipulation of files off-line.

— flow control

Where large amounts of data are to be transmitted to the terminal at high speeds and the user himself is down loading data, the buffer memory on the micro can be quickly filled up at a rate which is greater than that at which it can be down loaded onto the disk. This results in either data loss or corruption of the data itself. This problem can be avoided if the package provides flow control (X-ON, X-OFF). This ensures that a signal is sent to the host computer to tell it to stop further transmission until the terminal has sent a further signal indicating that it is ready to receive data once more.

In order to make flow control effective, the host computer or the data network used for the on-line information retrieval must also operate with flow control. Most hosts support the X-ON/X-OFF protocol. However, not all hosts transmit a unique end of transmission character, and some software packages cope with this by keeping a check on the time which has elapsed since the last character was received from the host computer. When this reaches some predetermined limit, typically 3 seconds, the system will assume that the end of transmission has occurred and will send the next line to the host computer. This particular feature is more directly related to data upload where it is necessary to interrupt transmission at any point in the search. This is much less a problem for hosts which support the X-ON/X-OFF protocol because each transmission concludes with an X-ON character, and once this has been received and recognised by the micro it can then send the next line of data to the host.

— other features

Other features useful to this type of communications include the ability to cope with telephone hang-ups, interrupt transmission of data from the host, and status indicators.

Most micro software/suppliers are able to provide assistance in choosing an appropriate package for a particular model and user requirements. Additional advice is available from the On-Line Information Centre, referred to earlier, who collect information about hardware and software currently being used to access on-line systems.

In general, most standard VDU terminals and printers, mini and microcomputers (including word processors) can be used for database access provided they conform to basic specifications. Although this will vary from one host to another a typical specification might comprise the following:

— ASCII compatible;

— asynchronous operation;

— 7 data bits (plus one stop, one start and one parity bit) per character;

— even parity;

— full-duplex mode;

— line speeds of 300 bps (30 cps), 1200/1200 bps (120 cps) or, 1200/75 bps (transmit at 75, receive at 1200).

With the availability of Telex/PSS gateway (InterStream One), users who only possess Telex terminals can now access on-line information databases. This is considered significant by many of the major hosts suppliers who are developing services worldwide, particularly in the third world countries.

In addition to a terminal for sending and receiving data a modem or an acoustic coupler is required to connect the terminal to the line. Micros today are increasingly being supplied with integrated modems either as an option or as a standard feature.

Modems can be rented or bought or may already be an integral feature of the micro. Modems can store and remember telephone numbers, identification numbers and passwords, and provide auto-dial facilities. Costs generally equate to the number of features and the line speed provided.

A 300/300 (V21) line speed is used mainly for small portable printers, eg the Texas Instruments Silent 700 terminal and other low cost simple terminals. The 1200/1200 (V22) and the 1200/75 (V23) speeds offer a much faster connection for information retrieval. Users of the V22 service, however, need a modem provided with error correction facilities to avoid corruption of data.

To complete the installation a telephone is required to send the information to and from the terminal. Preferably this should be a direct rather than a switchboard line, to minimise the possibilities of sessions being disturbed by line noise or disconnections.

THE COST OF ACCESS

For users located close to the host, direct dialling over the PSTN provides a reasonable cost access which only incurs normal telephone charges at local call rates. However, as the majority of hosts in the UK are located in London and the Home Counties, users in other parts of the UK are at a distinct disadvantage.

In the past, to ease this problem, some of the major hosts have installed their own private networks with local dial-up nodes in several of the major cities and other centres outside London. Normally there is no charge for the use of such networks apart from the local call charges for users who can connect within local call distances from the nodes. For users outside local call distances, PSS is increasingly being used as a means of access, and several of the host organisations are today dismantling their private networks and moving more and more users over to PSS (see Chapter 13).

For hosts without private networks, PSS provides the most cost-effective means of connection for the users located outside the local call charge area of the host computer site. Non-local users are, therefore, encouraged to dial into their local PSS exchange (or IPSS if outside the UK).

Overall, subscribers to the on-line databases are advised that they can save considerably on the cost of communications by using PSS if they are located a local call away from PSE and are assessing a host computer a longer distance away.

As an illustration, if it is assumed, based on real usage, that on a 30 cps terminal a typical user transfers 14 segments of data per minute (where one segment is equal to 64 characters), then the overall charge for using PSS (based on tariffs published in September 1984 and referred to in Chapter 3) is 2.02 pence (plus VAT) per minute during the normal office hours and 1.71 pence (plus VAT) per minute during the cheap periods. To this cost must be added the charges for calls to the local PSE.

To give a complete picture, Table 12.1 shows the cost of a typical 20-minute search using PSS for users located within the local call charge area of their local PSE compared with PSTN medium and long-distance calls, at different times of the day.

The PSS costs include the PSS and PSTN call charges (including VAT). Additional charges for dial-up access include: telephone line rental and

RATE	PSS	PSTN		
	local call to PSE	a up to 56Km	b$_1$ over 56Km over low cost routes	b$_2$ over 56Km
Peak	£1.16	£2.16	£3.61	£4.33
Standard	£0.96	£1.45	£2.71	£3.25
Cheap evenings/weekends	£0.59	£0.54	£1.08	£1.35

Table 12.1   Comparison of Cost of a 20 minute Search using PSS or PSTN

BT modem rental (if applicable) on the telephone bill; and NUI rental and facility charges (if applicable) on the PSS bill.

For users located outside the local call distance of the PSE, the PSS charges for the 20 minute search are increased as shown in Table 12.2.

RATE	DISTANCE FROM PSS NODE		
	local call	a up to 56Km	b_1/b_2 over 56Km
Peak	£1.16	£2.48	£4.50/£5.52
Standard	£0.96	£1.88	£3.50/£4.30
Cheap evenings/weekends	£0.59	£0.89	£1.41/£1.71

Table 12.2

The illustration we have looked at was for a user using a terminal with a speed of 30 cps. In general, if a user has equipment capable of working at a higher speed of 120 cps, then the overall search costs can be reduced. However, this usually depends on the user's requirements, particularly where the advantages of high-speed terminals are used to print out more information rather than, say, reduce the search time. Nevertheless, it is reasonable to assume a reduction in search time at high speeds such that in this illustration a search duration would fall to 10 minutes and consequently involve 28 segments (28 x 64 characters) of data transfer per minute. Table 12.3 gives the total cost of the faster and shorter search using the 120 cps terminal. The resultant savings in the total telecommunications bill can be deduced by comparing Tables 12.2 and 12.3.

	DISTANCE FROM PSS NODE		
	local call	a up to 56Km	b_1/b_2 over 56Km
Peak	£0.62	£1.28	£2.29/£2.80
Standard	£0.52	£0.98	£1.79/£2.19
Cheap evenings/weekends	£0.32	£0.47	£0.73/£0.88

Table 12.3

Looking further afield access can be considered to the US and Canada where a high proportion of the host computers are located. IPSS links into data networks such as Tymnet and Telenet in the US and to Data Pac in Canada.

As in the case of inter-European IPSS, access is via PSS but only a single international charge is incurred. The rates for inter-continental IPSS access, as would be expected, are higher than those for inter-European IPSS. Again, taking the 10 minutes search with the high-speed terminal as an example, the costs shown in Table 12.4 result for intercontinental information retrieval using International PSS.

	DISTANCE FROM PSS NODE		
RATE	local call	a up to 56Km	b_1/b_2 over 56Km
Peak	£2.63	£3.29	£4.30/£4.81
Standard	£2.53	£2.99	£3.80/£4.20
Cheap evenings/weekends	£2.28	£2.53	£2.79/£2.94

Table 12.4

The intercontinental IPSS charge used in this example is 3.5 pence per 10 segments and 10 pence per minute. For host computers located outside Europe, and North America, connection is through IPSS in exactly the same way but the the volume charge is 4 pence per 10 segments.

For all hosts located outside the UK only the single international charge for calls is made. Connection to PSS is covered by one set of charges comprising of the initial charge and quarterly rental for each NUI. Connections to UK hosts will, naturally, incur normal PSS charges in addition to the initial fee and quarterly rental for each NUI.

PSS DIAL-UP ACCESS SPEEDS

The dial-up access connection to PSS can operate at the following line speeds using a modem or an acoustic coupler:

— 110/300 bps;

— 1200/75 bps (split-speed);

— 1200 bps full-duplex.

The dataline access for character terminals connected to PSS can operate at the following line speeds:

— 110/300 bps (Dataline 300);

— 1200 bps full-duplex (Dataline 1200).

The 1200/75 bps split-speed option means that the user receives data at 1200 bps and sends data at 75 bps. This relates to a normal keyboard type of operation.

Mosts hosts connected to PSS and IPSS will handle terminals at all these speeds, as illustrated earlier. However, at the present time, the 1200 full-duplex access service for dial-up connection to PSS presents technical problems in some geographical areas such that the effective use of this service is prohibited. Under these circumstances, BT may advise the use of the 1200/75 service whenever possible for dial-up access until the problem is remedied.

Alternatively, a Dataline 1200 service could be used, or a modem with error correction facilities could be used to overcome this temporary problem.

Today, around 90% of users are still connected to on-line information hosts through slow (30 cps) terminals. But there is now a very significant swing over to the 1200/75 services for the cost saving reasons referred to earlier, and because of the enormous growth in the popular micro systems which are equipped with this specific communications capability. A move to the higher speed terminal (120 cps) together with a wish to send data at more than 7.5 cps has persuaded many users to adopt the 1200/1200 full-duplex connection but provided through the more reliable Dataline 1200 service rather than the PSTN dial-up service.

HIGH USAGE CONSIDERATIONS

For users who expect to generate high usage of the PSS connection for on-line information retrieval, it is likely to be most cost effective if dataline instead of dial-up access is used. Dataline does not use the PSTN and the terminal is permanently connected to the PSS network PAD. The terminal does not have to identify itself as it is automatically recognised by the PAD as having PSS access.

This immediately makes a dataline connection more attractive because it eliminates the dial-up call between the user and the PSE. This not only simplifies user access procedures but can result in cost savings because the distance-dependent and call-related local telephone charges are replaced by a fixed dataline connection charge and rental for the line and modems.

Obviously, such savings depend on the distance of the user from the PSE and the time of day but, typically, savings of between £1.00 and £5.00 could be expected on the 20 minute search illustrated earlier through removal of the local telephone charges.

In addition, further small savings can be expected on PSS call charges because lower tariffs apply to the duration charges for dataline access as against dial-up access.

However, against these savings must be offset the annual dataline rental. If this is costed solely to the on-line information retrieval usage then a considerable amount of usage is required, in the order of 60-80 hours per year to make a dataline worthwhile. The user will also have to be located a long distance from the PSE. If any nearer, then considerably more usage would be required.

In practice, however, the dataline costs may be spread over a number of other applications in addition to on-line information retrieval, thereby making this option much more worthwhile. For example many users of on-line information services today are able to access several host computers (typically 6) from a single microcomputer and, at the same time, avail themselves of electronic mail services such as Telecom Gold and Telex, over the single PSS connection and using the same terminal equipment.

Datalines also provide a more trouble-free service than the dial-up access, because being a dedicated link to the PSE they are less prone to the noise and interference problems which are often common on the PSTN. A dataline character terminal can also take advantage of PSS transfer charge acceptance and minicall facilities (described in Chapter 3), in addition to the CUG membership. Although these would not have an immediate application in on-line information retrieval their use may be very attractive for other types of application such as electronic mail services and connections to the public Telex network.

A consideration which could mitigate against the use of dataline access is the loss of freedom of access that is normal with the dial-up service. A dataline is a dedicated link to PSS so if users wish to dial direct to a local computer, or a private network not connected to PSS, an additional modem or acoustic coupler will be required for the dial-up line.

The full features of PSS and X.25 can be further exploited through the connection of a packet terminal instead of a character terminal to the dataline. This would be only true, however, if the extra cost for the X.25 software and hardware package is justified.

Manufacturer-supplied X.25 interfaces (ie PADs) are commonly available for asynchronous character terminals at a relatively low cost. For example, S-COM has implemented their PC-X.25 range of software modules to support X.25 applications. The software is available for use on the IBM Personal Computer or in a format suitable for linking with user supplied modules on Zilog Z80 systems. A line driver is available for the Zilog synchronous input/output channel, and a keyboard and screen handler are available for the IBM PC, which enable the PC to function as a private PAD on an X.25 network. The X.25 software implementation which conforms to the PSS interpretation of X.25 is available at a cost of around £1,000.

In some instances, this may be viewed as too high an overhead which together with the cost of the dataline connection could tend to negate the benefits to be derived from a full X.25 dataline connection for single stand-alone terminals. X.25 and packet switching, it seems, at the present time offer few advantages to single-user stations. In the future this is likely to change with the availability of support in the PSS MultiStream service for X.25 virtual circuit subsets at lower cost than the 'full' X.25 service. For locations equipped with multiple terminals, the additional cost of X.25 interfaces and leased line connection is easily absorbed in private network solutions. These situations may change in the future with the availability of X.25 dial-up services, through the InterStream Two gateway and extension of low-cost X.25 interfaces to a wider range of terminals.

Other savings can be achieved from the high usage of PSS through qualifying for the low PSS call charges during normal hours (between 8.00 am and 6.00 pm Monday to Friday). These apply when the volume of data transferred is greater than 1,500 Kilosegments or more than

1,000 hours in each quarter for each NUA. It is most unlikely, however, that this rate of usage would be achieved with on-line search alone.

EXPANDING HORIZONS

The requirement for access to on-line information services usually originates from and tends to be administered by a single person in an organisation, typically the Librarian or Information Scientist. Although this leads to a cost-effective use of the computing and communications resources and staff time in carrying out information searches, it often becomes more convenient and advantageous to provide individual end users of the information with direct access. In other organisations multiple access requirements will have developed historically as individuals have sought access to specialised information sources.

For example, one organisation in particular has professional staff who need access to worldwide databases for applications covering legal, scientific and engineering applications. Individual needs have been met by encouraging the use of dial-up PSS as the cheapest means of access to this information.

However, with an upward trend in usage and in the number of connections, it became necessary to introduce a more cost-effective arrangement and at the same time improve the overall level of service to the end user. This was achieved by concentrating users connected over the internal telephone (PABX) through a private PAD onto a dataline connected to PSS (see Figure 12.2).

In this installation no extra hardware was required apart from the PAD, the dial-up modems being retained for dial-up connection from the PABX extensions. The overall gain was the removal of the long-distance calls to the local PSE which was located in a 'b' call rate area, and the individual connection charges for each user.

Also end-user convenience was improved dramatically by using a private PAD implementation rather than the standard network approach. Fewer corrupted characters and more friendly log-on procedures together with a faster service are seen as providing for satisfied users. In particular, before the new facility was installed users had to go through the rigours of PSS access specifying terminal type, 'who is calling', destination address, etc, and, worst of all, they had to restate their identity each time they requested a new address.

The application and benefits of private PADs in the role typified in this example have been discussed in detail in Chapter 9. Although these are very common arrangements in other organisations, access to remote databases may be extended through the interconnection of private networks to public data networks via X.25 gateways (as described in Chapter 8).

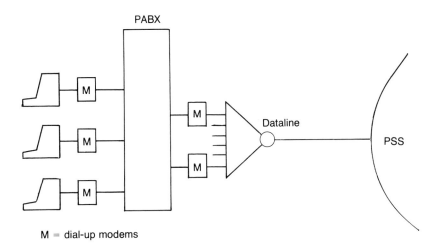

Figure 12.2   Private Network Configuration for On-line Information Retrieval

13 PSS in Value-Added Network Services

INTRODUCTION

Service bureaux have traditionally offered mainly interactive time-sharing computing often with specific business or scientific packages. Although the use of these services is still substantial, there has been a change in emphasis more recently with the development of powerful end-user computing facilities. This is encouraging many such organisations and newer organisations to extend and develop the range of facilities offered over their own private networks. For example, electronic mail services and private viewdata services are now being offered along with more traditional computing bureau services.

Such applications are prime candidates for public data services: for example, their geographic coverage can be immediately extended both nationally and internationally without any private capital expenditure or operational problems. The flexibility for accommodating such growth and to allow for change and peaks in traffic loads, together with the usage-dependent ties, means that the costs for both the network provider and the end-user can be kept to a minimum.

Private packet switching is already well established and used by many of the large bureaux. This trend is continuing as more organisations realise the benefits of X.25 packet switching as against the more conventional multi-point types of network. For such organisations in the UK, PSS, coupled with private packet switched networks, often provides the best solution; today several organisations with existing networks are in the process of dismantling their own networks as they move towards X.25 and PSS. For the smaller bureau or service provider, PSS, because of its distance-independent and usage-related charges, provides a very effec-

199

tive means of communications with users throughout the UK and the world. But above all it removes the burden of establishing a private networking infrastructure coupled with its inherent capital expenditure and operational responsibilities.

In our brief look at Telecom Gold we saw the illustration of a service provider using PSS to help provide an effective worldwide communications infrastructure at the launch of a new service. Other similar examples can be identified particularly in the areas of technical and financial information retrieval services. In the following pages, two case studies – one of a scientific bureau, and the other of a large network operator – are presented to illustrate the practical use of PSS within existing private networks.

In each of the examples, a description of the organisation and its network is given together with a summary of the 'Case for PSS'.

Any move to packet switching or PSS is a significant step and raises a number of issues of individual concern. For a given situation a number of key issues arise which are often established as criteria against which PSS and other networking solutions are judged. These include flexibility, performance and reliability, implementation, security, network management and cost issues; for each of these examples a number of such issues are discussed.

EXAMPLE 1: SCIENTIFIC BUREAU

Profile

In this example a scientific bureau provides a stress analysis design service using powerful number crunching systems which were primarily used for Government contracts but now are widely available to all customers in the UK and throughout the world. Today the organisation looks more like a software house and is getting more involved in design services with corresponding moves away from the powerful number cruncher towards more mainstream types of systems. For more demanding requirements, services are provided by a parent company in Europe which operates a very powerful scientific system. The organisation sees its bureau service becoming limited over the next 3/4 years and is, therefore, concentrating on developing its own network to provide facilities which will enable it to become a carrier for data traffic.

The organisation looked very seriously at the costs of installing its own network and took a decision to streamline its existing services by moving towards X.25. This is seen as providing flexibility in this particular business area, to accommodate new users and to make more computer ports available on the system to suit customer's needs. Consequently, the organisation has changed its mainframes over to X.25 and in doing so has cut down its overheads by taking out much of the existing dedicated hardware. This approach also provides tremendous flexibility in terms of accommodating various users with various terminal configurations. It also fills in the holes in their network node accessibility, and provides the advantages of X.25 facilities such as dynamic routeing and logical addressing.

The existing network was a statistical multiplexer system with major nodes at centres throughout the UK with spurs to all other major cities in the UK. The major trunks in this network make use of the KiloStream (X.21) service. The existing network was limited because it provided no contention facilities, being limited only to point-to-point connections. The X.25 solution is seen as providing a considerable gain in contention capabilities and speed matching of disparate terminals.

Why PSS?

The overall requirement was to make the network more cost effective and efficient. In the longer term this means dismantling the private network in favour of PSS particularly in the areas served by the smaller nodes where only low-volume traffic is encountered.

More effective use of networks is seen as a major advantage of X.25. In particular the powerful logical addressing and routeing facility of X.25 enables, in this instance, up to 600 users to be connected over a single internal control port.

This addressing capability also enables the network to be continuously and effectively monitored – which is a significant improvement on the statistical multiplex network originally used. The organisation had experienced considerable faults on their statistical multiplex network and this persuaded them to look seriously at X.25 and PSS.

The other significant attraction of X.25/PSS for this type of application is the facility to accommodate terminals of various types; in particular, the terminal automatic baud rate and speed matching facilities are an advantage.

This is particularly important because it allows services to be offered to a wide variety of users who have a wide selection of terminal equipment available.

Two other features of PSS which are of particular interest are the closed user group facility and itemised call information. By making use of the closed user group facility, users think that they are connected directly to the organisation and in particular their own service; moreover, they have their responsibilities lessened.

The availability of itemised call information enables the organisation to overcome a billing problem. Previously problems arose from trying to apportion service charges amongst customers with very different usage patterns. With the X.25/PSS operation, on completion of log-off the 'clear packet' information provides the necessary billing information for each call. There is, therefore, now no need to provide this facility on the original front-end processing system. This itemised information is now taken off the main on-line system and run on an off-line system to provide the necessary billing information for clients.

Overall the advantage of PSS to this organisation lies in its particular type of operation which is very well suited to the requirements of the type of service being provided.

Consequently, this organisation is implementing an X.25 network with private nodes and trunk facilities, and introducing PSS services for users who are located remote from the major nodes and who only make light use of the services.

Configuration

The configuration is shown in Figure 13.1. The existing private network is a statistical multiplexer system with nodes at several major cities and spurs to other centres throughout the UK. The major trunks make use of the 64 Kbps KiloStream (X.21) service.

A proprietary X.25 switch was chosen which had the ability to talk to the existing statistical multiplexers in the network using synchronous communication. The switch provides concentration/switching for terminals on the network for connection to hosts both in the UK and France; each connection provides for 15 logical channels (working on 2:1 contention ratio).

The IBM mainframe is front-ended by a 3705 communications control-

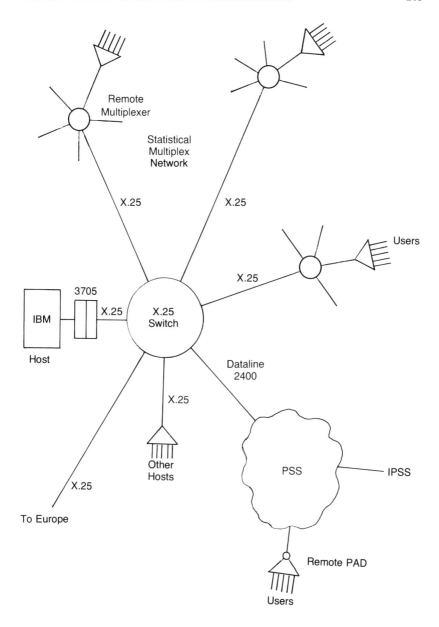

Figure 13.1   Scientific Bureau X.25 Network

ler to provide a 48 Kbits/s (X.21) service over the private TDM network. An X.25 program product (NPSI) operates in the controller in conjunction with the Network Control Program (NCP), to allow the SNA host to connect to non-SNA X.25 DTEs, PAD devices and non-standard PAD devices (eg the 2780 RJE system).

Because, with X.25, the front-end processor is not supporting as many channels, its overall performance is improved. For example, the communications load is lessened through a reduction in the servicing of interrupts.

The X.25 switch transfers calls over to PSS at level 3 through a direct connection to the PSE. In operation a 'call packet' on the switch is attached to a logical group and a 'welcome banner' is displayed back to the terminal; the asynchronous connection is then established to the IBM front-end processor.

In addition to supporting asynchronous terminals the network provides for 2780 remote batch connections. In this case the X.25 switch receives the calls from the statistical multiplexer and converts the synchronous signals into 'level 3' and then connects to the synchronous host computer (the 3705 which is front-ending the 3032).

The X.25 switch provides a 'gateway' for interconnection to PSS through a 2400 Dataline connection to the local PSE.

'Spoofing' of the IBM protocols (2780) is seen as providing a cost-effective means of communications through PSS. 'Spoofing' is the technique (outlined in Chapter 9) which includes the removal of communications overheads by stripping off control headers, etc; the presence of such headers, plus the X.25 headers, would incur unnecessary overheads in public data networks such as PSS.

A direct 9600 bits/s connection is provided to the French parent company, and alternative routeing can be provided over IPSS. In France the parent company operates an X.25 private switched network; from the UK the X.25 switch addresses this identity as a separate logical group. Further connection is made from the French network into systems in the USA.

Issues

Flexibility

With this type of service a very mixed population of terminals is encountered. In operation the user either adopts his own terminal profile or, if not, customises the PAD to suit. Because the actual terminal is not known initially, the host organisation lays down certain ground rules with respect to parity and data forwarding, and the recommended settings for these are specified. In addition, standard profiles are adopted for specific applications.

To cope with differences in X.25 in the various terminal configurations being supported, the 'qualifier' packet is utilised in the X.25 switch to configure it to the requirements of the remote PAD. The X.25 switch receives the call request, acknowledges and qualifies, and then reconfigures to the 'qualifier' packet.

Flexibility for expansion of the aggregate high-speed links through the allocation of further logical channels is seen as a key advantage of X.25.

Performance

With X.25/PSS, performance is effectively controlled by the flow control mechanism. However, high-speed performance and expansion capability are designed into the system. Consequently, asynchronous users experience no loss in speed. Synchronous users, however, create additional overheads by the nature of the protocols used which may in the future lead to problems which could affect the overall performance of the network.

Some users are aware of a buffering problem with PSS connections. For example, when carrying out a listing they have experienced a poor response to the STOP command. This is not seen as a major problem but some users dislike this buffering aspect of the service.

For this type of operation, error control is regarded as essential. For dial-in connections the weak link element of the network lies in the link from the terminal to the concentrator. For the customer who wishes to have a higher degree of protection and cannot tolerate loss in error performance, a facility is provided in the form of a remote error control box.

Reliability

The customer service has improved with the move to X.25/PSS in terms of increased reliability compared with the original multiplexer configuration. Previously reliability was a very big problem. With the new arrangement, one third of the network is under X.25 control because the addressing capability of X.25 enables the network to be continuously and effectively monitored.

Implementation

The original statistical multiplexer network was dismantled and the new X.25 network was installed within a period of 6 months.

The front-end X.25 (NPSI) on the IBM 3705 was easily configured. Customising of the NCP software was straightforward; it just required routeing tables to be established and features 'enabled' or 'disenabled'. The biggest difficulty was lack of knowledge on how to configure the system. The organisation considers that the X.25 documentation was very badly written and that support from IBM was minimal. The organisation had in-house support for the SNA architecture but had to work out the NCP requirements for itself.

Security

Security is important in this operation. There are specific users who require very secure connections, and therefore use encryption techniques for their application. X.25 is flexible, therefore not secure, so in this situation a connection straight into the mainframe is provided, ie without any switching. The lack of security in X.25 relates to the availability of NUAs which can easily be broken into by other users. Although the closed user group facility is used, it is not used for security purposes. Its main use is to simplify access procedures for new subscribers.

However, X.25 overcomes a type of security problem which was previously encountered in the billing of subscribers. With the older system, computer ports could be left open and could be contended into by someone else. With X.25 the SVC connection provides a virtual link on dial-up which drops out on disconnection. In addition every address is CRC checked and the danger of undetected 'flow-off' is minimised through the use of flow control procedures.

Network Management

This is a very important feature for this type of operation, as reliability is the key to satisfied customers. As mentioned earlier, using X.25 each physical or dial-up port is named. Therefore a single terminal can be used to talk to, to determine the status of, to attach to, or to monitor any device on the network from a single point. This was impossible with the point-to-point statistical multiplexer configuration because of its inherent inflexibility. Fault situations can now be looked at directly and the X.25 switch can be configured to take remedial action such as closing faulty ports, and reconfiguring the system.

The organisation feels that network management is an X.25 plus factor. Previously, a network control console was required; today, a terminal on the controller's desk can identify any fault anywhere in the network. This is possible through the X.25 addressing facility referred to earlier. With the statistical multiplexer system a terminal had to be brought alongside the device. The overall effect of this facility is the requirement for fewer support staff. Originally eight engineers were required to support the network; the present complement is down to two.

International

The organisation considers the PSS/IPSS connection of major importance in terms of offering the ability to extend their service to worldwide customers and also to provide alternative links into the French parent company and, eventually, into the United States.

Cost Components

The PSS package (Dataline 2400) includes the hardware components for the service connection to the X.25 switch from the London PSE. The cost of the remote terminal PAD to handle asynchronous dial-up and/or non-X.25 asynchronous connections is an extra.

For each remote node the cost of a dial-up group includes modems and rental of dataline, etc from BT. In addition, for each remote node site (usually customer premises), there are floor space charges, power supply costs and cable charges to be included.

There were no hardware additions to the IBM mainframe but a hardware board was required for the front-end processor and an X.21 interface board was needed in the X.25 switch.

The additional IBM mainframe software, the NPSI, was provided to support X.25 working. This was acquired on normal rental terms. Although relatively easy to configure, because of the minimal support provided by the supplier, a significant amount of effort was expounded in-house in acquiring an understanding of the product's requirements.

With X.25 no additional costs are incurred in terminal adaptation; adaptation is either by 'qualifier' packet or by customisation at the PAD.

By utilising the comprehensive addressing features of X.25, considerable savings in network management costs have been made through reductions in operational staff. In a sense cost savings such as these are not directly attributable to PSS because these facilities are an inherent part of the X.25 network.

Conclusions

This organisation sees X.25 combined with PSS as a way of providing more cost-effective and efficient networking services to its customers. Hence the decision to dismantle its private network in favour of the public data network; initially with low traffic volume nodes being replaced by PSS.

X.25 is seen as providing more effective use of the network through:

—   logical addressing and routeing features providing more effective use of the central computing capacity and network management;

—   flow control procedures providing the flexibility to accommodate a wide variety of terminal types;

—   facilities such as closed user group and itemised call information improving the overall service to customers.

All this adds up to significant improvements in the service together with substantial cost savings; for example savings of £100,000 have been achieved on capital investments compared with the original network configuration.

Currently problems with this approach include:

—   the effort required to support the X.25 implementation on the host;

—   the buffering problems apparent at customer's terminals caused by flow control procedures;

—   the lack of security over public data networks;

— the lack of error control and protection over local PSTN dial-up links to network nodes and PSS.

Although these are seen as problems with the present arrangement, they are considered of only minor importance by this organisation.

EXAMPLE 2: NETWORK OPERATOR

Profile

This organisation operates one of the country's largest commercial networks. The network provides comprehensive services for computers, electronic mail, videotex and timesharing applications. The electronic mail services and viewdata services have developed from internal requirements, these services are now being offered on a commercial basis. The organisation now holds a VANs general licence and has operated a private network for several years.

Why PSS?

PSS was initially used as a means of access to the electronic mail service. Today this access is not very common in the UK because of the growing availability of local nodes on the private network. However when there were less external nodes on the network, PSS was used as a convenient means of local access at a number of UK locations. At that time, there was also dial-up access across the PSTN ('b' rate calls for most subscribers).

Eventually the growing network provided coverage for the majority of user requirements, hence PSS access reduced to a minimum level. Today the major use of PSS is for international subscriber access to the electronic mail service.

For a travelling type of senior executive outside the UK, registration on the appropriate public data network (mainly within Europe and North America) provides an easy and convenient means of access to the electronic mail service. Also personnel in other parts of the world can make use of the international public data service to access their mailbox on the network. Several organisations make use of this electronic mail service (several hundred mailboxes) for their intra-mail services.

In addition to the extensive electronic mail services the network also provides a widespread videotex service with major access points in the main centres of the UK. At the outset, PSS was considered but it was decided that it would be an unworkable network for this service mainly because of the keyboard restrictions of the low-cost keypad on the viewdata terminal: these would not allow full PSS access procedures. Consequently the remote access requirement was met by the private network. The viewdata terminal has access to both videotex services and also access to the electronic mail system.

Although little use is made of PSS for access in the UK, PSS with its closed user group facility is seen as a convenient means of controlling free access to the service and can be offered as a pilot facility for new subscribers to the mailbox service. The network is registered as a closed user group to give the network NUI protection.

Configuration

The overall configuration is shown in Figure 13.2.

The network is based on a proprietary equipment and uses a proprietary network protocol provided by the vendor. The network which utilises switching statistical multiplexers provides a transparent service with local connections and is ideally suited for viewdata services. Within the network, X.25 interfaces are provided for internal applications with terminal interworking. A number of terminals are connected at 9600 bits/s and multiplexed over the X.25 logical channels by an in-house network PAD.

The electronic mail service is based on a DEC system. Ports are provided for connection to the network and for connection to PSS. The asynchronous to X.25 conversion for PSS is provided by a black box.

Viewdata is also available on dial-up via an X.25 link to PSS.

A gateway has recently been implemented to provide connections from the network into the public telex network. The gateway was specifically designed to accommodate differences of the telex service in various countries; interfaces provide a standard connection into the public network using a black box approach.

The gateway controls access to the network and provides functions such as security, protocol conversion and management control. Existing telex users are able to put messages into the mailbox but are unable to do more unless they make use of the full network messaging facility.

Synchronous terminals are currently handled separately; the network is purely for asynchronous traffic.

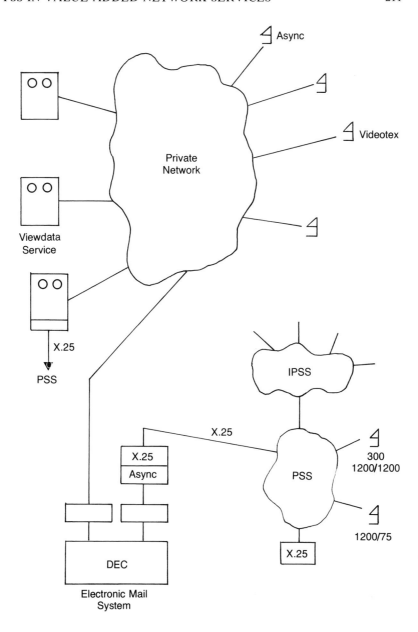

Figure 13.2   Use of PSS in a Large Commercial Network

The current network PAD (black box) which provides the PSS connection to the electronic mail system will in the future be converted to an in-house network PAD: the black box configuration will be thrown away.

At present synchronous communication is handled on a separate network over point-to-point links. Growth in asynchronous traffic on the network is known but growth in synchronous requirements depends very much on the future network capacity; for example, the use of digital circuits.

There is a possibility that access for areas currently outside the network – for example, the North of Scotland – may be required in the future. However, even though PSS may be considered as an option for this type of connection, eventually a further network node is envisaged to provide further geographical coverage provided there is sufficient demand for value added network services in this part of the country.

Issues

Flexibility

The major application for this organisation is the use of PSS for access to the network from international subscribers. In this respect the tremendous flexibility of PSS/IPSS is considered important in the sense of allowing any terminal in most parts of the world to access a system in the UK at a relatively low cost.

Although not directly related in this instance to PSS, the advantages of X.25 are recognised in the internal application. Using X.25 reduces the number of port connections and exploits the other facilities of X.25; for example, logical channel, virtual circuits, and speed matching.

Network Management

For PSS connections a subscriber either pays BT directly or a network NUI is offered. The network is registered as a closed user group to give the network NUI protection. This provides a convenient facility for controlling free access and can be offered as a pilot facility on the mailbox service. The use of NUI means that there is no concern over charges and the organisation is able to control free access for users. The requirement is for a valid name and password to be used when dialling into the network.

Implementation

The PSS connection is provided by a black box providing the X.25 interface to the DEC system. This approach was adopted rather than implementation of a full X.25/PSS interface because at the time (1981) this option was not fully available from the supplier. It was also considered that this implementation would have been too much of an overhead for the existing system. The aim was therefore to keep the interface to the network as simple as possible and to minimise the additional burden on the existing system; hence the black box approach.

It is unlikely that a full X.25 interface will ever be implemented on the DEC electronic mail system because there is a need to retain direct terminal drivers to handle individual terminals. The major drawback of this approach is considered to be the loss of X.29 services across the network.

Cost Components

The major cost item for the network was the black box to provide asynchronous-to-X.25 conversion for the PSS connection.

In the implementation of X.25 on the DEC system, apart from the additional DECNET and PSI requirements, a synchronous interface card is required at additional cost but on the other hand a number of asynchronous cards are redundant. At the time, these additional costs, plus machine loading problems, convinced this organisation not to implement the DEC X.25 interface.

Conclusions

For this large private network operator with substantial investment in its own nationwide resources, there is little benefit to be gained from using PSS in the UK apart from piloting services to new customers. The major use of PSS (although limited) is as a means of access via IPSS to the private network services for users either travelling or working outside the UK.

PSS was considered for the Viewdata service but was dropped because it was unable to support the simple keypad terminals used on that type of application. Unfriendly access is also a major criticism from organisations (such as the one described in this example) who feel that their customers want straightforward and easy-to-use connections.

14 PSS in International Networking

INTRODUCTION

With the tremendous proliferation of computer-based systems, many organisations are concentrating on bringing together all their computing and office resources into an integrated network. However, most organisations operate a variety of systems which are often incapable of communicating with each other. The cost of achieving a closer integration using the more conventional networks with private circuits can be very large. Similarly, the international corporation intending to integrate its operations worldwide often finds the communications costs are prohibitive. Other organisations may wish to consider extending their private networks by providing connections to the networks of other organisations such as their suppliers, wholesalers or retailers and perhaps the public.

In all these applications the major requirements are for low-cost communications together with the ability to attach and communicate with a variety of types of equipment and to cope with complex traffic flows between sites. As we shall see in the following examples, packet switching and PSS can often provide a solution to meet these requirements.

The first of these examples describes a large multinational organisation with a significant communications resource but needing to provide a simple and cost-effective means of communication to offices scattered throughout the world.

The second example examines the case of a UK subsidiary of an American parent company which required to integrate its European manufacturing operations through services stemming from its UK base.

The third example considers a smaller manufacturing organisation

215

which simply wished to establish a cost-effective and reliable data communications connection with its European subsidiary. The same format of presentation is used as with the examples described in Chapter 13.

EXAMPLE 1: MULTINATIONAL ORGANISATION

Profile

The requirement in this example is for international data communications from area subsidiaries and overseas agencies on a worldwide basis. These units are directly accountable to the UK Headquarters of the organisation and are required to make extensive use of a management information reporting system. This requirement applies particularly to the smaller units overseas who have little computing power but who are operationally responsible and required to report back on a monthly basis to the UK.

Previously the telex service was used for this function and eventually a connection was provided for direct input of data to the system in the UK over the telex link. A telex interface was introduced to provide a better facility for the service but this suffered from its inherent slowness. Further demands for more detailed accounting information made the organisation realise that the use of a telex terminal for this requirement was limited, mainly due to the imposed speed constraints.

Why PSS?

The basic need was to provide local functional computers, located in the various offices throughout the world, with communications back to the IBM Data Centre in the UK. A service from the US had previously operated on a dial-up basis at 1200 bits/s using terminals connected by asynchronous protocols; but problems with this connection arose, mainly due to modem incompatibilities and failure of the service caused by corruption and errors in the data transfer. This situation led to an investigation of PSS.

Configuration

A service was set up in the UK with a dataline connection from the local PSE to the front-end processor via a private PAD, as shown in Figure 14.1. The provision of this single dataline enables worldwide access to the UK host and the connection of any equipment operating at any speed

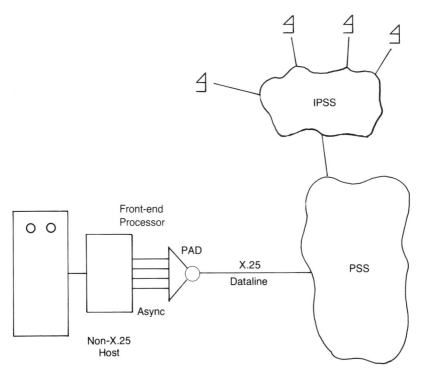

Figure 14.1 International Data Communications using PSS

in all parts of the world. The only onus on the user who accesses the
service from overseas is to make provision for connection to the PTT's
network and to negotiate individual requirements for the terminal
characteristics locally with the appropriate PTT.

Initially some difficulties were experienced in one of the offices in
supporting an IBM terminal which was already connected to the public
data network and used for word processing and data communications.
The problem lay with the IBM asynchronous software support for the
particular terminal. For future connections a preferred terminal such as
the IBM PC will be specified.

Future Requirements

In addition to asynchronous terminal dial-up access, a further application
is a requirement for a dial-up facility using IBM synchronous protocols.

This facility requires a PAD addressing requirement which is not currently available within the PSS network. The present solution would be to use a black box between the terminal and the network to establish the call and to allow full synchronous operation into the network by conversion from SNA to X.25 protocols. It would also require the X.25 implementation of SNA in the host computer front-end as described in Appendix 7.

Other future considerations include looking at the provision of synchronous communications from the other parts of Europe, using either distributed minicomputers or dial-up over the public packet switched network. As an alternative, the use of leased lines where traffic volumes justify the extra cost will be considered, but the high-cost penalty of leased lines in Europe is likely to make this unattractive.

It is felt by this organisation that the development of this type of application is hindered by the lack of support for synchronous devices in public data networks in Europe. Europe is not synchronous therefore initial handshake on dial-up is required using a black box solution with its associated overheads and costs. The availability of such support within public data networks in Europe, although at the discretion of the European PTTs, would be a welcomed feature.

Looking further to the future this organisation envisages up to 40 companies connected over PSS, and in the long term perhaps 200. The existing 2400 Dataline connection to the FEP which has eight logical channels will cater for the initial expansion. Further logical channels plus datalines will perhaps be needed as greater use of PSS occurs through the international activity.

Issues

Flexibility

In this application the flexibility of PSS is a major consideration in that it enables numerous asynchronous terminals to be logically mapped onto a single dataline with speeds matched over a range extended from 300 bits/s to 1200/75 bits/s. The virtual circuit concept in packet switching is seen to be a big factor in providing this degree of flexibility.

Performance

The performance of the service could only be compared with the previous telex service but nevertheless it shows a very significant improvement particularly for the end user. Some slight delay in packet transmission due to flow control is experienced; for example, pauses in packets are noticed at the end of certain characters. Such delays are not as apparent with the interactive types of operation as they are with file transfer operations.

Reliability

The PSS service is considered to be very reliable particularly for international communications compared with in this case the only real alternative of international dial-up. The only weak link in the PSS connection is the single dataline link to the PSE; this could be improved by adoption of the Multiline or 'alternative dataline to exchange' option if this becomes a major problem.

Implementation

The implementation of a separate front-end PAD was considered to be easier than the full X.25 implementation. The X.25-on-mainframe option was not seriously considered although X.25 was readily available and was proven for the IBM system. This was mainly because at the time the front-end processor capacity was restricted due to the age of the system, and because of the additional IBM software and hardware burden needed to upgrade the system.

The only real drawback through not having a full X.25 implementation lies in the area of virtual synchronous channels. X.25 software handles both synchronous and asynchronous channels. To implement synchronous channels in the present configuration it would be necessary to have a second dataline and a further black box to provide a synchronous connection to the mainframe.

One of the important advantages of the international PSS service to this organisation is that by using public data networks the implementor at the remote site needs to get involved in resolving local issues; the network is taken care of by the appropriate PTT.

Security

This organisation operates its own security methods in which they establish valid users of the service through the use of passwords, etc. As such they feel that they have the security provision of a large system and are happy with this situation; they therefore have no particular need for the closed user group facility of PSS. However, this may be reconsidered if in the future it is decided to provide connections from other distributed systems which themselves have only limited security features.

Network Management

Information is required on the use of the PSS service to enable the transfer of charges to the appropriate cost centres in the organisation. The organisation finds that the PSS bills are not fully detailed enough for this purpose. They require a bill listed in destination order. Although the on-line billing services and itemised billing are offered by BT, the PSS printout is not sufficient because of the need to manipulate the information given.

Although at present there is no requirement to implement network management on the private PAD at the computer centre this could become necessary as the network is expanded.

Cost Components

The cost of the hardware for connection to PSS (ie the modem) is included as a component of the dataline rental charges. (Dataline 2400 costs £1700 per annum.)

The hardware for the network interfacing is provided by the private PAD at an extra cost. The PAD is leased for a period of two to three years at a cost of around £1000 per annum including maintenance.

In this configuration no enhancements to the hardware or modifications to the hardware of the mainframe were necessary using the reverse PAD type of connection. None of the existing terminal hardware had to be adapted to connect into the network. Some changes were required in the procedures used to access the network, compared with previous procedures used by the telex service.

The initial service connection charges include the dataline connection charge and the charge for the NUIs. The PSS call charges are related to the international tariffs and are dependent upon the type of application. Typically a session of financial reporting (monthly) from New York costs $6.

Additional overheads have been incurred by the organisation through a slight increase in network administration caused by the need for extra staff to cope with the lack of detailed billing information. This typically requires up to two man-days per accounting period to process the information according to specific needs.

Conclusions

This company places particular emphasis on the performance of the International Packet Switched network as a data network which removes all the problems for the user, apart from the need for a simple local connection, irrespective of where he is located in most parts of the world. This is seen as being similar to the service provided for voice communications by international direct dialling over the public switched telephone network.

Overall, it is considered that PSS provides a high-performance service at low cost, for international networking. International leased line connections are considerably more expensive and dial-up costs are very high for this type of application. For example, a connection to New York which costs $30 to $36 per session using dial-up costs only $6 per session using PSS.

However, in the UK, it is felt that the long-distance telephone calls, which are often required to the local PSE because of their geographical unavailability, result in unnecessary high costs through most calls being charged at the 'b' rate. Both of these factors are today seen as making PSS much less attractive for networking at a national level although this situation is likely to change in the near future as the service expands.

An added bonus, if it were available from the PTTs, which would be warmly received by this organisation, would be network support for synchronous services (non-X.25).

EXAMPLE 2: LARGE MANUFACTURING ORGANISATION (EUROPEAN OPERATION)
Profile

Two years ago this company established itself in the UK with a worldwide data network for its European operation based upon the UK site. On-line systems were established on an IBM mainframe over leased lines to 12 major sites in Europe with links from the UK to sites in the United States.

Subsequently a further requirement emerged for communications with smaller offices in Europe. Dial-up, and multi-dropping using leased circuits, were seen as too expensive for this requirement and would not perform to the required specification. The particular need in this example was for synchronous communications at speeds no slower than 2400 bps to support displays and printers which are used for on-line enquiries, updating of information and batch reporting.

Data processing is established around the IBM environment. SNA is seen as a practical standard which provides a backbone network but at the same time the company is also keen to use ISO. In general, the network provides for sales-type applications including stock availability, order entry, enquiry and marketing forecasts. Further applications being investigated include the use of facsimile, electronic mail and integration of digital voice with data.

Links from the UK to the US and Japan provide for intercomputer links over the network for sales offices worldwide with access via the UK to the other services in the other countries. The US connection is provided over a transatlantic link using leased circuits.

Why PSS?

Although leased lines were used to connect to the larger offices in Europe they could not be justified in the case of the smaller sales office requirements. Dial-up access was examined but it was found to be too crude, too expensive, too error prone and not secure. Therefore PSS/IPSS was investigated as an alternative.

Call duration and distance related charges were considered to be a definite disadvantage with dial-up connections but with PSS/IPSS this was not the case because charges are distance independent and only usage related. Direct savings of £3000 per month were identified as likely if PSS/IPSS was used.

Consequently a service was set up with a Dataline 9600 connection from the local PSE to a packet switching interface (NPSI) on the IBM front-end processor (3725).

PSS was only considered viable for international links. It was not considered cost effective for other network links in the UK because the tariffs for leased lines are relatively low. This was in comparison with other European countries such as Germany, where leased line tariffs are higher and also where economic pressures are applied to push users towards public data networks.

Configuration

The configuration is shown in Figure 14.2. The synchronous terminals at the remote sites interface to the European packet switched services through the network interface adaptor (NIA) protocol converter which functions into the 3274 cluster controller. Offices throughout Europe will be connected in this manner as the appropriate versions of the NIA which meet the various X.25 interpretations in the different countries become available from IBM. At the host end a network packet switching interface (NPSI) is configured in the front-end processor. The NIA and the NPSI provide conversion from the SDLC to X.25 protocol.

Operation at a remote site requires the user to set up the link through the network on a key pad attached to the NIA. This is done first thing in the morning and the set up virtual call is maintained continuously for up to 10 hours daily. Although this procedure could have been simplified by the use of permanent virtual circuits (PVCs) these are not available over the international public data network connections. In addition to connecting further smaller offices throughout the various parts of Europe, a future application may involve the use of IPSS/PSS connections for back-up of the existing private leased line network to the major office sites.

As new offices are established, considerable use is made of telex, facsimile and telephone services. To make more use of the spare capacity on the private network an internal electronic mail system was introduced on the mainframe when the network was established. A private electronic mail service was set-up initially to the major offices to make greater use of the network but within a short time of its operation a demand arose from the smaller offices for access to electronic mail services. This was mainly due to the advantage to be gained in overcoming time zone problems by the use of the store-and-forward facility which overcomes a very difficult communications problem present in most international business operations.

The increase in traffic due to this demand for electronic mail has established greater justification for the connection of other smaller office

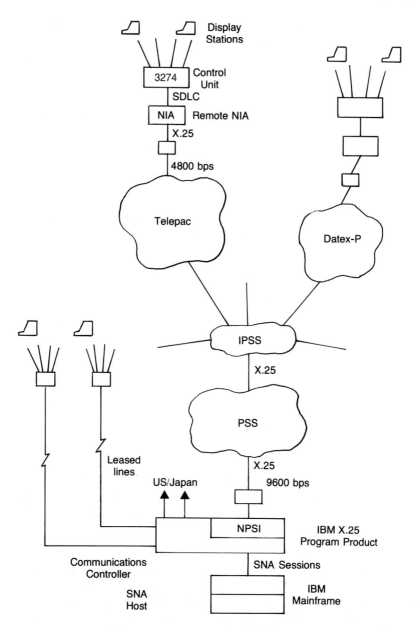

Figure 14.2   Using PSS for the European Connection

sites onto the network because of the savings which can be achieved over the existing telex and telephone services.

Issues

Flexibility

In this example, flexibility, in terms of providing for a scattered and varied terminal operation, is not regarded as a major issue because this does not arise with the corporate computing strategy adopted by this organisation.

Performance

This organisation considers that the performance over PSS/IPSS connections is not as good as that over the leased lines but this is more than offset by the substantial cost savings referred to earlier. With regard to the overall performance of PSS/IPSS three major problems have arisen:

— the inconvenience of establishing and disconnecting links;

— the newness of the X.25 technology in terms of product availability;

— a significant loss of speed which has resulted in a poor response time.

Of these, the poor response time is considered to be the most significant factor affecting overall performance; it therefore warrants further discussion.

For 3278 displays which comprise 24 x 80 characters a full display of 1920 characters requires 16 packets of 128 characters (2048 characters total). Though in practice only changes on the screen or blank screen characters are sent, this effectively means an update of 1000 characters is typically required. This requires seven to eight packets for a full screen presentation.

A total time of up to 10 seconds is required for the transfer of the eight packets. This comprises three seconds for the first packet plus one second for each subsequent packet (this includes the time from the initial request plus an allowance for the mainframe response which in general accounts for the three-second initial delay).

This situation, which is considered to be just acceptable with a small number of displays connected, becomes much more of a problem as this number increases. A leased line connection on the other hand gives a much better response time and is more consistent when it is required to connect many more displays.

This degradation in response time over PSS/IPSS routes is considered to be more than offset by the substantial cost saving benefits referred to earlier. However, the inconsistencies which occur as the number of displays are increased may impose constraints on future expansion plans and encourage greater use of private leased lines.

This organisation suspects that limitations in the International Gateway on IPSS which limit the effective throughput may be a contributory factor towards the problem of increased response times. It also feels that, on international calls, loss of the PSS window size selection facility – which means that acknowledgements are sent following the transmission of three packets – creates overheads which affect overall performance. The loss of the closed user group facility over international links also raises security issues; these are discussed later.

Reliability

From initial experience with this application, reliability in terms of the loss of connections has not been as good as that for the leased lines due to international link problems. Normally one disruption per month lasting for a couple of hours is experienced with this type of connection.

Implementation

Implementation was fairly straightforward although setting up the service caused some difficulty mainly due to misunderstandings which arose in agreeing the details of the service with the various European PTTs. This related to specific parameters in the network characteristics such as packet size, window size, time-out, and network address, which had to be set-up for each NUA and agreed with the appropriate PTT. Support was required from the PTTs and in each case some slight changes were required.

Support for the synchronous operation came from IBM. It is felt that the cost of this item could have been reduced if the PTT networks provided both X.25 and IBM interface facilities, including synchronous protocols.

Security

In this application, security of operation would ideally have included use of the closed user group facility but this is not available over international links. The company considers that it has a secure system, however deliberate sabotage through the public network remains a possibility and hence there remains a need for a closed user group facility if it were available.

Network Management

Network statistics are not automatic with this system: only manual records are maintained in the network management centre. With little network management information available a classical multi-vendor fault situation can arise on the loss of connections. But as more connections are made, a better indication and a feel for fault situations is being established. In addition, more proficient management of the links together with the use of existing on-line diagnostics available on the system provides more information on fault situations. However, the attainment of 100% availability is not seen as a major requirement with this organisation because it is accepted that the additional costs would not really be justified to maintain the required level of service.

Cost Components

The cost of hardware, ie the modems, for connection to the service is included in the dataline rental.

The provision of the network interface in terms of the NIA is an extra cost incurring a rental of around £200 to £300 per month for each NIA. No mainframe hardware enhancements or modifications were required.

No additional network management costs were incurred as the organisation makes considerable use of the existing capability which was already provided in the original system configuration. In this respect the use of packet switching now makes better use of this facility.

Additional mainframe software in the form of NPSI was provided to support the X.25 interface. This is a standard product and was provided at a rental charge of £160 per month.

In addition to loading in the new software module, changes had to be made in the control program to support the NPSI; this was done by the organisation itself. The requirement here was for special education (one man-day of effort) plus the time required to make the changes to the control program and to load in the additional software module. Here this need for specialised support was not a major hurdle as this type of resource already existed in the organisation.

The initial service connection charges were the normal PSS charges. No charges for facilities were made because these are not available through the international links. Apart from the rental charges identified above, the operational costs include the rental of the dataline. Rental also covers all the maintenance costs.

Conclusions

In this example, this large organisation with a fairly substantial invest-ment in networking found that PSS/IPSS provided a cost-effective method of communications to its small offices in the major countries of Europe to which leased circuit provision could not be justified. The facility was installed with a minimum of effort and delay, although exten-sive in-house technical support was at hand for implementation of the X.25 software.

Specific problems arose in agreeing the details of the service with the various PTTs in other countries, with the loss of PSS facilities across the IPSS gateway, and with the unfriendly access procedures. The major drawback, however, has been the apparent degradation of response time compared with the leased line connections. Although this is possibly due to current restrictions in the IPSS gateway referred to earlier, a further cause of the problem can be apportioned to the IBM method of imple-menting X.25 on polled networks, which was discussed in Chapter 9.

EXAMPLE 3: SMALL MANUFACTURING ORGANISATION

Profile

This organisation is a small manufacturing company based in the UK and with a subsidiary located in France, with an annual turnover of around £2 million.

When it was set up, the organisation installed a system to carry out ledger processing, sales order processing, order history, and order entry. The initial system was a single-user machine but this was later expanded into a system with several display units, greater storage capacity, tape handling, and line printing facilities.

More recently it was decided to investigate the use of X.25 for connection to the Paris office of their international subsidiary. The requirement was for a limited but regular transfer of data files, together with interactive working on a daily basis for both order processing and enquiries.

Exact information on the required usage volumes and the number of transactions and duration of each on a daily basis (order processing and enquiries) was obtained. With this information available, the leased line and PSS/IPSS options were considered, with the following conclusions:

— leased line connections – cost £16,000 per annum and subject to delays on connection;

— PSS – cost £8,500 per annum (plus connection charge) with immediate connection.

Why PSS?

Clearly PSS/IPSS provided the most cost-effective and available means of communication to the international subsidiary. The alternative leased line option was dismissed because of the higher costs involved and the delays on connection.

Configuration

Consequently a service was established with a Dataline 2400 connection from the local PSE to the host system in the UK. As shown in Figure 14.3, the configuration in France comprises 4 terminals and a printer with a concentrator linking into the TRANSPAC service. As an alternative, displays with X.25 system capability were considered but, for internal reasons, it was preferred to provide a stand-alone computing facility in France. Additionally, the concentrator in France allows copies of print files run in France to be sent from the UK with console commands issued from the UK.

At the host end, an X.25/PSS implementation was configured using an X.25 interface module to provide the communications processor with the ability to connect to X.25 public data networks. This facility allows

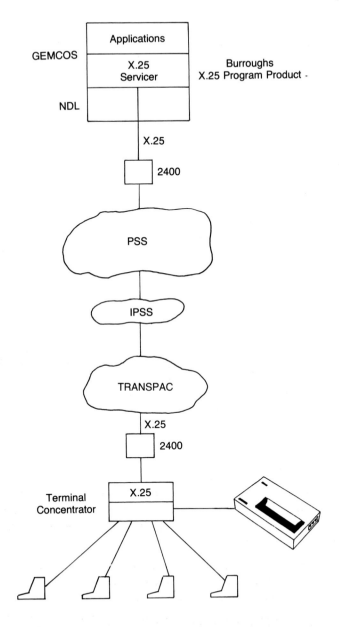

Figure 14.3   The French Connection

application programs to communicate with compatible application programs in other X.25 packet mode DTEs. The module takes care of all the functions of packetising and depacketising, virtual circuit establishment and breakdown, and also provides procedures for communication of application programs with non-packet mode DTEs via the X.29 PAD device recommendations. This approach required no modifications to the programs although an internal timing penalty was incurred.

The remote concentrator functions as a full packet mode DTE terminal emulator. X.25 is added to the message format which in itself is fixed to avoid additional carriage costs across the network.

A particular requirement of this application was for the system program to be arranged to set up all calls in France (to establish virtual circuit connections) so that the calls would be billed at the French end. This was arranged to meet the accounting procedures of the organisation.

Issues

Implementation

The provision of the software and PSS presented no problems and overall took one month to implement. The X.25 software was installed in less than a day although this required considerable support from the supplier. The PSS dataline was quickly and easily installed by BT. However, subsequent delays were experienced in getting the service operational at the French end mainly due to problems in agreeing details with the French PTT.

Cost Components

The cost of the hardware, ie the modems, for connection to PSS is included in the dataline charges. Other network interface costs lie in the additional communications provision required on the remote terminal concentrator in France.

The UK-based mainframe required an additional communications line adaptor for this implementation at a cost of £1,800 plus the additional X.25 software module at a cost of £1,200.

The operating costs include the dataline rental charges plus the PSS call charges (estimated as £8,500 per annum).

Conclusions

In this example, PSS is clearly identified as the most cost-effective and easily available service for data communications between the UK and France for the type of traffic (relatively low volume and 'bursty' in nature) encountered in the applications described. This is a typical requirement for many small/medium-sized organisations operating in the UK and Europe today which has led to a substantial application for PSS.

The installation of the X.25/PSS connection including the X.25 interface was quickly and easily implemented and at relatively low cost (the X.25 interface itself cost less than £2,000). The only major drawback was the problem of liaison with other PTTs apart from BT, which in the end extended the ready-for-service date.

15 Evaluation Guidelines

An organisation preparing to evaluate the possible benefits of X.25 and PSS should first define its intended use of products and services. Points which have arisen from the case studies examined in the preceding chapters and which should be considered in this definition are summarised below:

— are both terminals and computers to be involved in the application, or just computers? Applications involving terminals will usually require consideration of protocol conversion issues;

— does the existing software provide the necessary integrated X.25 interfaces and host linking software or will these be written for the application? If the software is to be written it can take advantage of the special features of both X.25 and PSS and the characteristics and tariffs of PSS. Existing software may have to be modified at additional expense and upheaval. Alternative approaches using emulation ('black boxes' which present X.25 to PSS but which make the host computer believe it is connected to a conventional network) may provide an expedient and less costly solution but do not fully exploit the X.25 facilities. Guidelines for the implementation of software on host systems to support character terminal access via PSS is given in the PSS User Forum SG3 'Green Book', referred to in Chapters 8 and 9 and described in Appendix 5;

— is the computing and terminal equipment to be used already installed or will new equipment be purchased? New equipment can be purchased with X.25 compatibility. Existing hardware may need special attachments for X.25 support such as interface boards and line drivers, if such support is available from the supplier;

— is there adequate in-house expertise in data communications especially in computer networks and X.25 itself? Without staff experience to support it, the implementation of an X.25 application can be difficult. Organisations without this experience should carefully examine the supplier's ability to provide this type of support;

— what network geographical coverage and traffic volume growth is projected over the next five years in the application under consideration? Both PSS and other public data networks outside the UK cover varying geographical areas, and tariff structures may favour some areas over others. Additionally, large data traffic volumes may cost-justify dedicated private network solutions. Growth from a limited to large data traffic volumes suggests a possibility of migration from a public network to a combination of public and private packet switched communications.

— are there any related applications which may become candidates for the sharing of the communications facilities? Many organisations find that communications systems often attract secondary applications which may have differing requirements to the primary application; other potential applications should be examined for effects on traffic volumes and differences in functional requirements.

16 Summary of User Experience

Because of the relative newness and unique features of PSS compared with those of the traditional services, it was inevitable that time would be needed for users to assess the benefits of PSS and its wider implications, and for PSS to acquire a particular slot in the marketplace. It is not surprising therefore to find that there is a significant and growing number of users who have found PSS to provide the most cost-effective vehicle for dial-up access to on-line information services and to timesharing services, particularly over long distances and over worldwide international packet switched services. These are the very applications with those traffic characteristics that favour the packet switched type of service. The benefits to be gained from using PSS are largely self-evident, and also the conversion from dial-up to PSS is relatively straightforward, as was illustrated in the previous examples.

This type of application is gaining greater momentum with the increasing availability of national and international public data networks, the development of more sophisticated and attractive network services and the rapid growth in the use of low-cost micro technology. Coupled with the access to information and timesharing services is the increasing use of single devices to provide access to other related business services, such as Telex and electronic mail, over a single dataline connection. This provides a more cost-effective use of the facility which in itself encourages greater use of PSS. Opportunities for this type of usage have been furthered by the provision of gateways on the public networks.

A further significant and growing application of PSS is in the area of international networking. As we have seen in the example described in Chapter 14, many organisations appreciate the benefits of PSS and IPSS for providing a cost-effective and reliable means of data communications throughout the major civilised communities in all parts of the world. More recently this has become a significant area of use through the growth of public data networks in the majority of trading countries throughout the world.

However, almost from the beginning, PSS was seen as having an extensive and significant role as a cost-effective vehicle for a whole range of new applications. Today organisations are now in the process of looking seriously at these wider opportunities. Two examples which we have described earlier are CHAPS, the interbank high-value cheque clearing system, and the credit authorisation system implemented by the major credit card companies and BT.

Further growth in areas such as these is expected as PSS broadens its capability through future enhancements and expansion plans, to take on new applications. Of particular note are value-added network services such as electronic mail and other message services (for example, Teletex and electronic funds transfer services) and specific industry networks.

Although given the appropriate application characteristics such as on-line information retrieval, PSS is a cost-effective alternative to PSTN, particularly over distances which exceed the local dial-up radius of the serving exchange. The evidence for PSS as a less costly alternative to leased circuits within the UK remains inconclusive. It is still too early to expect a significant migration from established private networks given the substantial capital investment in the latter and the cost of conversion. Although there is no real evidence that many users are seriously contemplating replacing private circuits by PSS, there is – as illustrated in the previous examples – a trend, particularly with information services providers, to replace less economic elements of private networks with PSS connections. There is also a growth in the use of PSS by similar organisations who are embarking on providing such network services for the first time. These developments have been encouraged by the expanding availability of PSS as a public access network throughout the UK. This was a situation that did not exist a few years ago.

Because private network economics involve a very detailed consideration of alternative designs, it is much more difficult to develop generalisations as sharp as those advanced by PSS as a direct PSTN replacement. For simple dedicated point-to-point links it currently seems unlikely with the present tariff structures that PSS could be competitive for other than the low traffic volumes and low communications-intense applications described earlier. Applications with high traffic volumes and/or high performance requirements, and for which public switched service capability is not the prerequisite, favour the private circuit approach.

It should also be remembered that according to the current BT marketing strategy, PSS is not primarily intended as a substitute for traditional services, but rather as a complementary service offering quite different facilities. In this respect, PSS is not regarded as a direct substitute for private circuits, mainly because PSS is a public switched service whereas private circuits are not. Indeed it is argued that the two should not be compared on a cost substitution basis alone. Private circuits, PSS and circuit-switched services are three distinct categories of service with different tariffs and facilities, and each affords different opportunities.

In identifying the sources of cost savings which have been described for PSS, the distance-independent tariff element in the tariff structure has the most significant impact in transmission costs, and this is further enhanced by the usage related elements.

The features of PSS which are particularly attractive to users and which have a strong influence on their decision to use it are the contributions made by X.25 and its associated protocols. Flexibility in resolving equipment incompatibilities is seen as a significant factor in terms of the initial connection and thereafter in future network expansion. The ability to easily handle changes in traffic patterns is seen as another attraction of the X.25 connection over the more traditional arrangements, particularly as cost savings are often identified. Further savings can often be established with the X.25 connection because of the much simpler interface arrangements required at the host end.

These advantages are seen as particularly attractive for organisations providing network services to a wide and varied customer base. Other related benefits include extensive geographic coverage worldwide, and growing within the UK, and the attraction of an established and managed network. This latter feature is regarded as an essential requirement for organisations without their own networking resources and for those who wish to shed many of the responsibilities associated with any such function.

Network management facilities are seen as a major benefit as are the high reliability and low error rates which have been experienced by many users of the PSS service. This is a significant consideration for users in the financial and banking sector where reliability is a major component of overall system security.

For the individual terminal user, PSS provides a means of easy and error free access, with immediate connection to remote services at relatively low cost from an increasing number of areas of the UK. This is achieved without substantial investment or technical demands being placed on the user. PSS also provides a gateway to an increasing number of other national and international public networks from the most simple and low-cost type of terminal device.

All this paints a 'rosy' picture of the PSS service; but what about the other side of the coin?

On the basis of a limited look at user experience during the preparation of this book, a number of problem areas have been identified. The most significant of these are as follows:

— under current tariff relativities the evidence suggests that private data networks handling large traffic volumes are unable to economically justify migrating to PSS; the major deterrent is the traffic (volume) component of the tariff particularly for fixed price applications;

— users and prospective users of the service are frequently concerned about the unfriendliness of the access procedures and lack of data security in asynchronous connections. There is also considerable comment being expressed concerning the lack of support in the public network PADs for devices other than simple asynchronous terminals. Of special interest is support for Viewdata terminals and non-X.25 synchronous devices;

— for dial-up users the limited availability of local connections to PSS due to lack of local access facilities often leads to long-distance call charges; this is seen as a discouraging factor. The alternative dataline connection is not always considered an attractive alternative because the dataline charges cannot always be justified in terms of traffic carried; this is of particular concern to the small business and professional user;

— for international connections the performance of the service especially in terms of response times is affected by the limitations of the present IPSS gateway which restrict the effective average throughput of each individual channel to around 2000 bits/s. Also the loss of PSS facilities across the IPSS gateway often penalises the effective use of international services;

— although not directly a problem of PSS, the implementation of X.25 interfaces on host mainframes through expedient solutions, rather than by complete adaptation of operating systems and existing teleprocessing software, results in less than optimum system performance. Of such solutions the implementation of X.25 and interfacing software on a front-end processor provides a more effective answer than emulation, although emulation is often adopted in the short term as the simplest and least costly approach.

If further investigation and other evidence were to confirm the validity of these statements then a question arises 'What could be done to make PSS more attractive?'. On the basis of the evidence presented in this book the following steps might be considered to remedy some of these problems:

— introduce changes to the present tariff structure including traffic volume discounts and 'package' deals which are not totally related to usage;

— expand the network and include the provision of lower levels of local access with associated reduced access charges for local connections with an eventual move towards local free access;

— extend the provision of PSS facilities across the international gateway and improve the throughput of the gateway;

— introduce PAD facilities to support a wider range of access methods, a simplified X.25 for stand-alone terminals, and error protection on asynchronous terminal connections.

Most of these considerations are included in BT's announcements of plans for the enhancement and development of the service. This suggests that this is the way of the market. If so, it will be interesting to see if the market now responds to what can be regarded as a new era for PSS. Without doubt, such enhancements will radically change the economics of data networking in the UK.

Although primarily concerned in this book with PSS it is not possible to disassociate from the development of X.25 and packet switching. Within this area a key element is the type of support adopted by the major computer manufacturers for X.25 in their products. Evidence to date suggests that this support has only been provided in rather a reluctant manner and often without a real commitment to designing optimum solutions.

It is accepted that there are major difficulties for suppliers in following this path in terms of the incompatibilities with their existing protocols and product ranges, the implications for existing product ranges and the implications of the progress of work in the development of OSI standards. Nevertheless it can be argued that more impetus towards X.25 in this area would give rise to improvement in the overall performance of packet switching solutions, and thereby encourage much more effective use of PSS.

In conclusion, PSS appears at the present to satisfy particular data transmission needs, as illustrated in this book. With increasing user experience, together with the planned expansion and enhancement of the services within the network, its role will continue to develop.

Individual users need to carefully evaluate the service and decide for themselves whether the benefits outweigh the upheaval of migration. They should also consider, on the other hand, whether they can afford to delay using a service which is often a springboard to wider national and international communications, and the basis for the development of new commercial opportunities and initiatives in their own organisation.

Appendix 1

Bibliography

A major source of further information is the descriptive literature produced by British Telecom; in particular, the references listed in Appendix 4 of this book which refers specifically to the PSS and IPSS services. Further references which supplement this information and the material in this book are listed below.

Bleazard G B, *Why Packet Switching?*, NCC Publications, 1982

Bleazard G B, *Evaluating Data Transmission Services*, NCC Publications, 1983

Bleazard G B and Roberts J, Users Give Thumbs-Up to Packet Switching, *Management Review*, Sept 22, 1983

CCITT Yellow Book, Volume VIII – Fascicle VIII.2, Data Communication Network Services and Facilities, Terminal Equipment and Interfaces, Recommendations X.2-X.29, CCITT, VIIth Plenary Assembly, Geneva (November 1980), pp 649-657

CCITT Yellow Book, Volume VIII – Fascicle VIII.3, Data Communication Network Transmission, Signalling and Switching, Network Aspects, Maintenance, Administrative Arrangements, Recommendations X.40-X.180, CCITT, VIIth Plenary Assembly, Geneva (November 1980)

Character Terminal Protocols on PSS (Green Book), Study Group 3 of the British Telecom PSS User Forum, 1981

Design Notes for PAD Implementors, Character Terminal Implementors Group of British Telecom's New Networks Technical Forum, March 1984

241

Deaton G A and Hippert R O, X.25 and Related Recommendations in IBM Products, *IBM Systems Journal*, Vol 22, Nos 1/2, 1983

Gee K C E, *Introduction to Open Systems Interconnection*, NCC Publications, 1980

Gee K C E, *Local Area Networks*, NCC Publications, 1982

Gee K C E, *Proprietary Network Architectures*, NCC Publications, 1981

Going On-line, On-Line Information Centre, 1984

Handbook of Data Communications, NCC Publications, 1982

Hardy P, *Digital Private Circuits for Data Communications*, NCC Publications, 1984

Lane J E, *Corporate Communications Networks*, NCC Publications, 1984

Lane J E, *Review of British Telecom Services*, NCC Publications, 1982

Norton M J, Public Data Networks Today, *NCC Office Technology and Communications Circles Joint Conference Proceedings*, February 1985

Packet Switching and X.25 – A Status Report, Datapro Communications Solutions, Vol 1, 1984

Telecomms Equipment & Service Directory, Comm Ed, 1985

Thorning G, Implementing Private Wide-Area Packet Switching Networks, *Proceedings Telecoms Today, International Conference*, 1984

Appendix 2

Useful Addresses

Enquiries concerning PSS should be made to:

MultiStream and Packet SwitchStream Customer Service Group
G07 Lutyens House
1-6 Finsbury Circus
London EC2M 7LY
Telephone: 01-920 0661 or FREEFONE 2170 or FREEFONE Multi-Stream

Requests for further information about international services should be made to:

IPSS Marketing Customer Services
British Telecom International
Room 723 Holborn Centre
120 Holborn
London EC1N 2TE
Telephone: 01-936 2750
Telex: 21601 BTIG

Appendix 3

Glossary

Call Accept
A Call Accept packet confirms the called party is willing to proceed with the call. It does not normally carry user data, except in a converted minicall (see **Minicall**) and is not needed on a permanent datacall.

Call Redirection
Allows call to be automatically passed on to a nominated address when the intended recipient's terminal is not operational.

Call Request
A Call Request packet is sent to initiate a datacall. It may carry up to 16 octets of user data. It is not needed on a permanent datacall.

CCITT
International Telegraph and Telephone Consultative Committee. A body which makes international recommendations for telecommunications.

Character Mode Terminal
A data terminal equipment that does not have the intelligence to comply with Level 3 interface procedures and requires the assistance of a Packet Assembler/Disassembler to communicate with other Public Data Service terminals. It will operate asynchronously at up to 300 bits/s or up to 1200 bits/s.

Circuit Switching
A method of communications in which a connection between the calling and called stations is established on demand for the exclusive use of the circuit until it is released.

245

Clear Request
Information transmitted by a DTE to terminate a virtual circuit with another DTE.

Closed User Group (CUG)
Optional user facility which permits user equipment belonging to the group to communicate with each other, and precludes communication with any user equipment not belonging to the group.

Cyclic Redundancy Check
A block checking method in which the numeric binary value of a block is divided by a constant divisor. The quotient is discarded and the remainder serves as a Block Check Sequence (BCS). The transmitting station calculates and transmits the BCS; the receiving station compares the transmitted remainder to its own computed remainder and finds no error if they are equal.

Datacall
An ordinary call on PSS. Synonym for the CCITT term 'switched virtual call'.

Datagram (DG)
A self-contained message packet requiring no connection procedure between the sending and receiving end (employed in X.25 packet switched networks).

Dataline
A dedicated link between the customer's terminal and the PSS exchange. Includes a modem on the customer's premises, a line, a modem at the exchange and a port. Operates at the bit rate indicated by the associated figures (eg Dataline 2400).

Data Transfer Phase
Phase of a call on PSS during which data packets may be sent. A minicall has *no* data transfer phase. A permanent datacall is *always* in the data transfer phase.

D bit (delivery confirmation bit)
A bit (bit 7 of octet 1 in an X.25 packet header) used to request end-to-end acknowledgements for data transfer (using the packet receive sequence numbers).

Dial-Up
With reference to PSS, means using a telephone and the Public Switched Telephone Network to gain access to the PAD in the PSS Exchange.

DNIC
Data Network Identification Code: the user's number in a public network.

DTE (Data Terminal Equipment)
Equipment such as terminals or computers at which the communications path either begins or ends.

Duplex
Full duplex working means that a terminal can transmit and receive simultaneously.

Echoplex
A mode of operation in which user-entered data is echoed on a character-by-character basis.

Flag Sequence (frame level)
The unique 8-bit sequence 01111110, which delimits the start and end of a frame.

Frame
The sequence of contiguous bits bracketed by, and including, start and end flag sequences.

Frame Check Sequence (FCS)
The field immediately preceding the ending flag of a frame containing the bit sequence which provides for error detection by the receiver.

Frame Level Logical Interface
The interface involved in the administration of the physical link between the terminal and the network node.

General Format Identifier
The four high-order bits of the first octet in an X.25 packet header, containing the qualifier bit, the delivery confirmation bit, and the modulus value.

High Level Data Link Control (HDLC)
Bit-orientated data link control procedure defined by the International Organisation for Standardisation (ISO).

Information Field (frame level)
The bit sequence between the last bit of the control field and the first bit of the frame check sequence. The contents are not interpreted at the frame level.

Interrupt Confirmation Packet
A packet sent in response to an Interrupt Packet.

Interrupt Packet
A packet used to send control information end-to-end, notwithstanding
the use of packet level flow control. May be sent after detection of a
Break signal.

ISO
International Standards Organisation.

Kilosegment
One thousand segments.

Layer
The International Organisation for Standardisation (ISO) nomenclature
for protocol classes in open network architectures (see also **Level**).

LCI (Logical Channel Identifier)
An identifier which specifies a particular permanent or switched virtual
circuit. The LCI is divided into the Logical Channel Group Number and
the Logical Channel Number.

Level
The International Telegraph and Telephone Consultative Committee
(CCITT) nomenclature for protocol classes in open network
architectures (see also **Layer**).

Link Access Procedure (LAP)
A frame level protocol between the PAD and the network node to which
it is connected, defined in X.25. It is a subset of the HDLC procedures
specified by ISO.

Link Access Procedure, Balanced Mode (LAPB)
A frame level protocol between the PAD and the network node to which
it is connected, defined in X.25.

Logical Channel
An apparently continuous path of communication to or from a packet
mode terminal. The number of simultaneous communications possible on
that terminal is the same as the number of logical channels.

Logical Channel Group Number and Logical Channel Number
Specifies the route a packet will take through an X.25 packet switched
network, contained in the first and second octet of the packet header (12
bits).

M bit (more data bit)
A bit in the Packet Type identifier of a data packet, indicating that additional packets will be sent in the same packet sequence.

Minicall
In PSS the minicall is a short message (up to 128 octets) on the 'call request' packet.

Modulus Value
Defines the packet receive sequence number [P(S) and P(R)] sequence and maximum packet length; values of "modulos 8" and "modulos 128" are defined in Recommendation X.25.

Multiline
More than one dataline between a customer and his PSS exchange, where all have the same network address.

Multiplexing
Carrying more than one data 'message' simultaneously over one physical link or circuit. There are several different multiplexing techniques; PSS uses 'unassigned time division multiplexing'.

NUA
Network User Address. A unique 12 digit number by which each terminal on the PSS network is identified. It is used for directing a call to a particular terminal and identifying a calling terminal for billing purposes. Packet terminals have the option of two further digits for sub-addressing at the terminal's location.

NUI
Network User Identity. Required only for dial-up access. A code which must be quoted on each occasion before calls may be made.

Octet
Eight consecutive bits of user data, eg a character

Open Network Architecture
Data communications networks that do not use physically dedicated transmission paths between end-use equipments.

Packet
A unit of data, address, and control information with a fixed maximum length. A packet may be a complete message in itself or one of a series.

Packet Assembler/Disassembler (PAD)
Performs protocol conversion and packetising functions for terminals incapable of performing these functions.

Packet Header
The first three octets of an X.25 packet.

Packet Switched Network (PSN)
A data communications network in which data is transmitted in packets.

Packet Terminal
A terminal which is capable of forming its own packets and interacting with the network.

PAD Parameters
A set of variable values which define the way the PAD gives its assistance and which may be selected for any given character terminal or call.

PDN
Public Data Network: in Europe usually supplied by the local PTT.

Permanent Datacall (PDC)
A channel between 2 designated addresses. Data may be sent at any time without the need to set up a call. Synonym for the CCITT term 'Permanent Virtual Circuit' (PVC).

Permanent Virtual Circuit (PVC)
Effectively a point-to-point, non-switched circuit over which only data, reset, interrupt and flow control packets can flow.

Physical Interface
The physical connection between the DTE and DCE.

Port
The point at which signals from a terminal enter and leave a PSS exchange. (Also applies to communication processors generally.)

Protocol
A set of rules or instructions for carrying out a particular function – X.25 has a three-level protocol.

PSE
A PSS exchange.

PSTN
Public Switched Telephone Network.

Q bit (qualifier bit)
A bit (bit 8 of octet 1) in an X.25 packet header used to distinguish between control commands and user data for PAD connected terminals.

Reset Request
The method used to restore the flow control on a virtual circuit to the same state as when the circuit was established.

Restart Packet
Equivalent to sending a Clear Request on all SVCs and a Reset Request on all PVCs, ensuring that all calls are in the initial state.

Segment
The chargeable unit of volume on PSS. One segment is 0-64 octets of data.

Statistical Multiplexing
A method of communication path sharing in which information is inserted into the transmission stream as it (the information) becomes available.

Switched Virtual Circuit (SVC)
A virtual circuit through the network which exists only as long as the call is maintained.

Terminal
With reference to PSS, a terminal is taken to mean any device which generates data. Corresponds to the CCITT term 'DTE'.

Terminal Profile
The default values of the PAD parameters for a given terminal.

Transfer Charge Acceptance
Programming of BT equipment to enable receipt, in appropriate cases, of transfer charge calls, which may then be either accepted or refused on a per call basis.

User Facilities
Functions such as reverse charging, Closed User Group, packet and window-size negotiation, etc, implemented on packet switched networks.

Virtual Call (VC)
A temporary virtual circuit set up for the duration of a data transfer.

Virtual Circuit
A logical transmission path (through an X.25 packet switched network) established by the exchange of set-up messages between two DTEs. Virtual circuits may be temporary or permanent (see also **Virtual Call, Permanent Virtual Circuit**).

X.3
The CCITT recommendation defining the functions performed by, and operational characteristics of, the PAD for start/stop mode user equipment.

X.25
The CCITT recommendation defining the interface between DTEs and DCEs for asynchronous terminals operating in packet mode.

X.28
The CCITT recommendation defining the interface between a start/stop terminal and a PAD.

X.29
The CCITT recommendation defining the interworking between two PADs.

X.121
The international packet switched network numbering scheme.

Appendix 4

BT Descriptive Literature for PSS and IPSS

PSS Descriptive Literature

Packet SwitchStream information pack   – PH3689
(a folder containing all PSS brochures)

MultiStream information pack   – PH/NN 35

Basic Guide and Directory   – PH3395

First Steps in Packet Switching   – PH2828

Packet SwitchStream Technical Guide

Packet NetMux   – PH3425

Enquiries about the current availability of PSS literature should be directed to the address given in Appendix 2.

IPSS Descriptive Literature

General descriptive leaflet

— IPSS Meeting Business Challenges of Today and Tomorrow

— 'Visitor's Service' leaflet

— IPSS cards (details of routes and countries available)

Appendix 5

'Green Book' Recommendation on the Use of X.3, X.28 and X.29

The 'Character Terminal Protocols on PSS' as defined by Study Group 3 (SG3) of the BT PSS Users Forum in document SG3/CP(81)6 (The Green Book) contains a recommendation which aims to provide guidelines for implementors of software on host systems to support character terminal access via PSS.

The recommendation also considers the wider problems associated with character terminal access on private networks connected to PSS and the design of 'private' PADs. This is currently an interim recommendation for protocols to operate over the ISO Session Service issued by the Focus Committee on Information Technology Standards.

As described in the chapters of this book, the operation of the PSS PAD which adheres to the 1980 version of the CCITT Recommendations is determined by the values of a number of parameters (currently 18). These parameters are defined in X.3, and their values can be changed both by the character terminal user and by the host application program at any time during a call to alter the operation of the PAD.

The 'Triple X' Recommendations do not suggest modes of working or specify which of the parameters the host or terminal should be allowed to change. The Working Group considered that frequent modification of the values of PAD parameters by either the host or user would lead to confusion between the two ends and was unnecessary for most applications. For example, there are many makes of terminal which are either buffered, or will echo characters automatically; in such cases it is pointless for the host to attempt to echo input characters remotely by manipulating the relevant PAD parameters.

The 'Green Book' aims to overcome these types of problems by recommending modes of working and rules for changing the values of the parameters. Recommended modes of use of X.3 parameters described allow values for each of the parameters together with an indication as to whether the host or terminal user may change the values and under what circumstances. Two modes of use are identified; 'message mode' where detailed control of the terminal is the responsibility of the PAD and 'native mode' where the PAD acts as transparently as possible and detailed control of the terminal is vested in the host. The implementors of host facilities are strongly recommended to limit their use of X.3/X.28/X.29 to these modes so as to ensure successful interworking; the predominant mode of use envisaged is the 'Message Mode'.

Recommendations for Host Implementors are given concerning the use of the X.25 virtual circuit, the use of X.29 control and data messages and the changing of X.3 parameters. The general principle is that the host should accept as wide a range of variants of the protocol as possible, but should only generate commands and data within a defined subset. For example if the host terminates the session, it should normally send an X.29 'Invitation to Clear' message rather than an X.25 'Clear Request' to ensure delivery of all remaining output messages. If the PAD does not clear the call within a reasonable time period then a 'Clear Request' should be issued. It is also recommended that hosts should avoid sending PAD messages wherever possible as PAD messages cause forwarding of data from a standard PAD and may confuse local editing. With regard to data sent to or received from the PAD (X.29 Data Messages), one recommendation states that, in the Message Mode, hosts should assume that echoing, editing and padding functions have been performed by the PAD, and should not duplicate these functions.

The circumstances under which parameters should be changed by the host together with a summary of the initial values and when they may be changed are specified as referred to earlier. Additional recommendations relate to the sequence of actions to be taken when the parameters are changed by the host.

Recommendations for Users of Standard PADs cover the use of X.28 and include the use of PAD commands, the data transfer state and the changing of PAD parameters.

The PAD Service Request (speed and profile selection) will set initial values for all parameters. A 'V series' of profiles is defined to provide suitable values for a recommended subset of X.3/X.28/X.29 for most common terminal types.

On connecting to the PAD, the user selects a profile which corresponds most closely to the terminal used. Any special requirements are set up before the call is made using a 'Set' or 'Set' and 'Read Parameters' command. If uncertainty arises over the setting of the PAD parameters through error conditions in the host or deliberate or accidental change by the user, then the original profile can be reset by use of a PROF command.

The call can be established and controlled through the use of the Selection, Clear Request, Reset Request and Status Request commands.

The main problems which may be encountered by the terminal user in the data transfer state concern the nature of the forwarding rules and lack of transparency to all input characters. Where normal Message Mode forwarding or forward on all control characters will not meet all requirements applications should still be usable by employing EOT (CTRL/D) as a send key to force forwarding.

Problems of non-transparency of input characters may be encountered on standard PADs with several characters including DLE (CTRL/P), X-ON (CTRL/Q), X-OFF (CTRL/S) and DEL. The recommendations suggest that host systems which employ any of these characters should choose a replacement character to duplicate the function for access over PSS.

These parameters which may be changed by the terminal user and the circumstances under which they may change are shown in Table A5.1.

Although the main part of the recommendations covers the interworking of hosts with standard PADs conforming exactly to the PSS specification, an annex to the document provides guidelines for the implementation of 'private PADs'.

It is considered essential that a minimum subset of X.3/X.28/X.29 be defined that a host can expect all private PADs to support. It is also suggested that there are some additional facilities which may be provided in a private PAD without jeopardising its ability to communicate with an X.29 host, but which will improve the performance offered to the user.

These facilities include additional private PAD parameters and guidelines on methods to allow entering of any character as data, additional presentation facilities for VDUs, parity checking on terminal connection, and support for additional profiles.

Parameter	Initial State	Circumstances of Change
2 Echo	(on)	for half-duplex terminals
5 Flow control by PAD	(off)	for buffered terminals
9 Padding after CR	(profile)	for non-standard terminals
10 Line folding	(profile)	for non-standard terminals
12 Flow control by terminal	(off)	for buffered terminals
14 Padding after LF	(profile)	for non-standard terminals
15 Editing	(enabled)	
16 Character delete character	(decimal code of delete character)	to allow editing characters to be entered as data
17 Buffer delete character	(decimal code of delete character)	
18 Display character	(decimal code of display character)	

Table A5.1

The annex also lists some undesirable features of the standard PAD which it is suggested could be implemented differently in private PADs. For example:

— a switch to command mode by the terminal user or receipt of a PAD message from the host causes forwarding of data in the standard PAD. It is recommended that this should not occur as it

prevents subsequent editing of the forwarded characters and is
likely to lead to considerable user confusion;

— input is echoed immediately by the PSS PAD and may be
interleaved with output characters. It is recommended instead
that input and output are interleaved on a message basis;

— if the PAD supports terminals with a line length greater than 128
characters then it should allow editing on the whole line and it
should not automatically forward on the packet full condition;

— to avoid the user having to re-specify an NUI for each connection
made, a log-in/log-out mechanism independent of call management is desirable.

The final parts of the recommendations for Private PAD Implementors
discusses support for the host-PAD connection and for the terminal-PAD
connection. Compliance with the X.29 Recommendation is demanded
with a few additions, exceptions and clarifications. The commands and
responses given in Recommendation X.28 or the PSS Technical Guide
are not considered sufficiently 'user friendly' for general use. An alternative set of commands is given.

As discussed in the chapters of this book the CCITT Recommendation
X.29 explicitly makes use of the facilities and formats of X.25 for the
transfer of messages between host and PAD. Extended use of
X.3/X.28/X.29 is a problem in situations where multiple interconnection
networks are envisaged (due to the limited addressing capability) and
where support for X.25 is not available. A Network Independent Transport Service has been defined which insulates the higher applications
from the underlying communications media and also provides an
extended addressing scheme which overcomes the limitations of X.25.

In accord with this work the Working Group defines an encoding of
X.29 on the Transport Service. Called TS29, this protocol preserves the
same control functions as X.29 but overcomes the limitations referred to
above. The Network Independent Transport Service (Yellow Book)
referred to in Chapter 8 of this book, also prepared by the Study Group 3
of the PSS User Forum, defines the specific Transport Service referred
to in the definition of TS29 contained in the annex to the 'Green Book'.
In addition to providing an outline specification of the TS29 protocol,
the annex contains a description of the rules of conversion between X.29

and TS29 at gateways interconnecting networks at the Transport Service level.

A number of networking products support the recommendations contained both in the 'Yellow Book' and 'Green Book' particularly for applications which are within the academic world. One product, the JNT-PAD, was developed by CAMTEC in collaboration with Cambridge University and the Universities Joint Network Team to meet the requirements of X.3/X.28/X.29, to implement the 'Green Book' recommendations and to provide 'Yellow Book' Transport Service addressing.

The University of York UNIX-X.25 package which enables a host computer running the UNIX operating system to connect to X.25-based networks includes a 'PAD' program which follows the spirit and recommendations of the 'Green Book'.

Appendix 6

Open Systems Interconnection

INTRODUCTION

The purpose of Open Systems Interconnection (OSI) is for a computer, terminal or program to be able to communicate with any other. Ideally, each partner should not need to know the technical characteristics nor the supplier of the other. All that is required is the knowledge that each is observing the same conventions and standards for exchanging information. Openness refers to the acceptance in the use of these standards and not to any loss in confidentiality on the part of the systems involved.

Before the advent of computer communications, open systems were not required in computing. Most customers were confident to buy the bulk of their computing equipment from the manufacturer of their main systems, or from other suppliers who made it their business to emulate this manufacturer's devices.

Things changed rapidly, however, when on-line working became accepted by the users and the data transmission networks appeared on the scene, but as long as the communications needed remained within the realm of each separate organisation, the interconnection problems, although quite substantial, were still solvable. It was the introduction of public networks which really prompted the development of OSI because they provided the opportunity for interconnection on a scale never before possible with computers. With public data networks there is no way that all the devices connected to it can be made to conform to all the standards necessary for information to be exchanged and understood.

But OSI is not just concerned with public data communications. Within an organisation OSI frees the user from the need to buy equipment from

the one supplier. The user can pick and choose devices with more freedom than before as well as being able to interconnect previously incompatible systems.

REQUIREMENTS OF OSI

It is worth exploring the requirements for making systems interwork
before explaining the details of the OSI model.

OSI implies much more than just physical interconnection of equipment. Just because a computer terminal from one supplier uses the same
plug and socket arrangement as a computer from another supplier does
not guarantee that the data format, speeds or even the pins used on the
plug are compatible. OSI requires that the devices must be able to
interwork as well as interconnect, by which is meant that information sent
by one can be understood by its recipient.

Three essential ingredients for interworking are required:

A *physical data transmission system* which all participants can use.
The purpose of a data transmission network is to transmit data
reliably, and preferably also cheaply and quickly.

Compatible dialogues. One user of a network should be able to
understand what the others are saying. To do this each must adopt
the same high- and low-level protocols. In human speech, communication takes the form of certain well-understood ways of
speaking, as well as the actual contents of the words themselves.
Humans are adaptable and sensitive to subtle changes in intonation,
etc and as a result they can easily understand a message even when
some normal conventions are altered. In computing we must
observe much more stringent conventions, otherwise the devices
involved may try to send out of turn or will misinterpret the information.

Applications. Certain applications are ideally suited to open systems interconnection. Within a single organisation which is widely
dispersed geographically it is likely that many computer systems will
be interconnected to provide a distributed computing system or just
access to a central installation. Once open systems interconnection
standards are more widely used, new applications will also be found,
especially in the field of inter-company transactions.

These three requirements can roughly be divided into processing-oriented functions, communications-oriented functions, and physical data transmission (Figure A6.1).

The process of dividing functions into logically separate groups is called layering and it is frequently used in designing computer systems. The only difference between layering a self-contained computer system and a computer network is that the latter always consists of more than one interconnected but otherwise distinct systems. Any one layer extends over all the systems involved.

The processing-oriented functions are concerned with the ability of two systems to exchange information and understand it. The rules required to achieve this co-operation are the high-level protocols.

The communications-oriented functions are concerned with the use of the physical data transmission system, and the rules associated with its use are the low-level protocols.

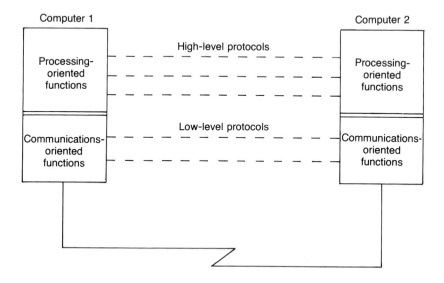

Figure A6.1   High- and Low-level Protocols

THE ISO REFERENCE MODEL

The International Organisation for Standardisation (ISO) began work on standards for open systems interconnection in 1977. Their first priority was to devise a standard architecture (called the Basic Reference Model for Open Systems Interconnection, defined in IS7498) which could be used to provide a basis for the development of the standards needed, whilst allowing existing standards to be accommodated where relevant. It also provided a method for dividing the work up into manageable portions so that separate teams could work on specific protocols and services. It was not intended to constitute a standard architecture which could be used to define an actual implementation. Nor was it intended to provide a yardstick by which proprietary network architecture could be judged. The purpose was to use it to provide a stable foundation for the development of the protocols necessary for open systems interconnection.

In practice the Reference Model has been used by some computer manufacturers to provide the framework for their proprietary network architectures. The ISO Reference Model naturally reached a fairly stable state before any high-level protocols or services were defined. Thus, computer manufacturers decided that it was sensible to use it and to place their own proprietary protocols within its framework, with a view to replacing these where necessary by the standard versions which will eventually be agreed.

Since layering had proved to be a successful technique for computing and communications functions, the ISO Reference Model was designed as a layered structure consisting of seven functional layers and a physical transmission medium (Figure A6.2). Each layer is self-contained and only the interfaces to adjacent layers, and the service it provides, need to be fixed. Each layer uses services provided by lower layers in order to carry out its functions. Functions within a layer but in separate systems communicate with each other using protocols appropriate to that layer. No protocol acts across layer boundaries.

The physical medium in Figure A6.2 joins the systems involved. It is usually the PTT-supplied network, although it could be private, such as a local area network. Using CCITT terminology, the boundary is usually the boundary between the data circuit-terminating equipment (DCE) – the modem for example – and the data terminal equipment (DTE) – ie the subscriber's terminal or computer.

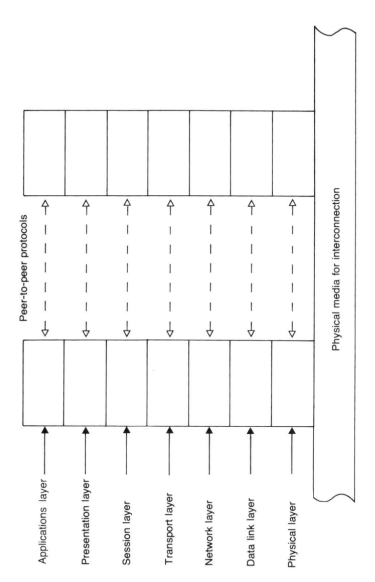

Figure A6.2   ISO Seven-layer Reference Model

Briefly, the functions of each of the layers are as follows:

Physical layer

This provides the means to interface the computer equipment to the physical medium, and the method to control its use.

Data link layer

In recognizing that physical transmission media are subject to errors (such as clicks and buzzes familiar to all telephone users), data link protocols were introduced some time ago to enable errors to be detected and corrected, usually by requesting retransmission. High-level data link control (HDLC) is a typical example. The data link layer of the ISO Reference Model is concerned with these functions.

Network layer

The network layer is required to provide the means to exchange data between systems by connecting individual data links together to form a network.

Protocols already existing in this layer, such as level 3 of X.25, can be used provided they are suitably enforced with a supplementary network protocol. Several networks of this character can then be interconnected into a single global network linking the two systems involved in the data transfer. The network layer thus becomes responsible for routeing between the systems and for providing relaying between adjacent networks.

Transport layer

The transport layer provides, in association with the layers below it, a universal transport service which is independent of the physical medium actually in use. Users of the transport service request a particular class and quality of service, and the transport layer is responsible for optimising the available resources to provide the service requested. Quality is concerned with data transfer rate, residual errors allowed, and associated items. Class of service covers the different types of traffic which diverse applications require; eg batch or transaction processing.

The transport layer always provides an end-system to end-system service, unlike the layers below it which may be concerned only with specific parts of the complete path interconnecting the systems. Thus the end-systems involved must agree to use a common protocol and service before data exchange can take place. Reflecting the different classes of service, several protocols are needed for this layer.

The transport layer can use multiple parallel connections to achieve the desired quality of service, or it can multiplex several concurrent sessions over one transport connection.

Session layer

The session layer establishes logical communications paths between applications or users wishing to exchange information. Two applications must form a liaison for this purpose, called a session. The session layer establishes, breaks and maintains the liaison, and ensures that data reaching a system is routed to the correct application. It also ensures that the information exchanged is correctly synchronised and delimited so that, for example, two applications do not try to transmit simultaneously.

Presentation layer

The presentation layer performs the two-way function of taking information from applications and converting it into a form suitable for common understanding (ie not machine-dependent), and also presenting data received to the applications in a form they can understand. The layer provides services which give independence from internal character formats, and consequently it provides machine independence.

Applications layer

The highest layer defined by the ISO Reference Model is the applications layer which is concerned with supporting the applications which exchange information with others. Many different types of application are relevant to open systems interconnection, from terminal-to-computer transaction processing to interconnected real-time process-control computing. Some of the protocols associated with this layer will be concerned with particular types of application, and others will be for general application program support.

THE STANDARDS SITUATION

Open Systems Interconnection is concerned with defining all the standards needed to achieve interconnection of systems and exchanging information. Many standards will ultimately be needed, so a major task has been defining where these are required.

The reference model is now an international standard (IS7498) but this by itself does not enable unlike computer systems to interwork. Within each layer, one or more service standards are being defined, and then, at the next level of refinement, the individual protocols to provide the service will be needed.

Currently, the OSI network service, transport service and session service have reached the Draft International Standard stage. This means they are technically stable and very unlikely to change before becoming a full International Standard. At the same stage of development are parts of the transport and session protocols. In addition some existing protocols, particularly in the network layers and below, are being used or enhanced as necessary to provide the defined OSI service. Of special interest is the work to enhance X.25 to make it become a truly OSI network protocol.

X.25 AND OSI

When it was devised, X.25 defined a protocol for connecting packet mode terminals (ie computers or similar devices) to public data networks. It pre-dated the OSI work and was for one particular type of network so it did not exactly map onto the model.

As described earlier, X.25 has itself a layered architecture. Level 1, the lowest level, is concerned with the physical characteristics of the interface between the packet terminal and the packet switching exchange (PSE). In this it corresponds to layer 1 of OSI.

Level 2 of X.25 provides the mechanism for managing the link between the packet terminal and the PSE, and for reliably transferring all the packets between them. X.25 defined HDLC as the basic mechanism for this, although two versions of level 2 were defined, LAP and LAPB, with differing HDLC commands.

Level 3 is the most important part of X.25, this being concerned with the packet format, procedures for setting up calls and communicating with other packet terminals.

Figure A6.3 shows the version of X.25 defined in 1980 mapped onto the OSI reference model. The current status is that the enhanced specification of X.25 (1984) extends level 3 to map onto the OSI network layer service definition. However until PTTs and manufacturers adopt the latest version, the OSI network service will still require the so-called X.25 (1980) Convergence Protocol to provide the correct level of service in this layer.

SUMMARY

One purpose of OSI is to give freedom to someone setting up a network to use whatever equipment is most appropriate. This feature will become more relevant when heterogeneous networks are in more common use. In these it will be possible to choose the hardware and associated software systems most appropriate to the intended user of the system.

Another use for open systems interconnection is to give users the opportunity to send data to, or receive it from, other organisations. Many new applications could be made possible by this facility. Currently, agreements between the organisations involved have to be made, not only to send and receive messages from each other, but also on the formats and protocols to use. Open systems interconnection standards will remove the need for agreeing the formats and protocols.

Since open systems interconnection covers both computing and communications it is a very important subject in relation to network architectures. The current trend is for newly designed proprietary architectures to be closely matched to the ISO Reference Model. Some older architectures are being adapted to become compatible, and provide functions not previously included. We can expect the general trend towards open systems to continue since most computer manufacturers have declared their support for the concept. Note should be made of the fact that each manufacturer interprets the open systems interconnection model in the context of his own products and customer requirements.

The open systems interconnection Reference Model in itself does not provide for true interconnection of systems – it only provides the framework for standard protocols and services which must be implemented in order for one system to be able to talk to another. Although interconnection is not the only requirement for interworking, it

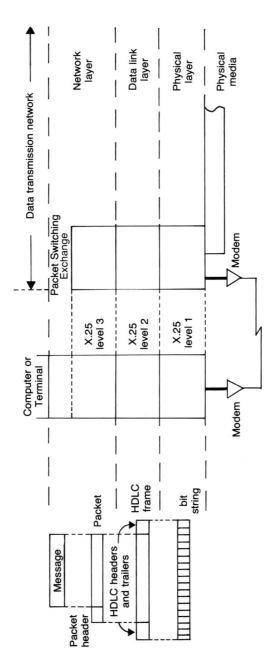

Figure A6.3   Relationship between X.25 (1980) and the Reference Model

is necessary. A proprietary architecture which is not functionally compatible with the Reference Model for open systems interconnection will not be able to communicate with one which is.

Appendix 7

X.25 in IBM Products

(Much of this description is extracted from *IBM Systems Journal*, Vol 22, Nos 1/2, 1983.)

INTRODUCTION

Having participated in the development of X.25, IBM announced in 1977 an attachment capability of several DTE products for packet-switched data networks (PSDNs) in Canada and France. Since that early announcement, IBM has enhanced its X.25 product offerings and extended support to many additional countries. IBM products that have the X.25 interface comply with the 1980 version of X.25.

IBM's X.25 products operate in accordance with Systems Network Architecture (SNA). SNA defines formats and protocols governing interactions among IBM products that are components of the SNA network. The implementation of X.25 in IBM products allows connectivity of SNA, and in some instances non-SNA, products through a packet-switched data network (PSDN).

ARCHITECTURAL RELATIONSHIP TO SNA

Public packet network services provide an alternative method for transporting user information. However, application requirements, geographical considerations, and applicable tariffs often dictate the choice of services and facilities for transporting information. Therefore, virtual circuits are managed in SNA in a manner consistent with the management of real circuits. Such management allows concurrent use of other services and facilities offered by telecommunication administrations, recognised private operating agencies, and companies providing common carrier or value-added telecommunications services around the

273

world. Relationships between SNA and X.25 are defined for two types of connection:

— SNA-to-SNA connections that allow SNA X.25 DTEs to be connected to one another by permanent virtual circuit services or virtual call services, or both;

— SNA-to-non-SNA connections that allow SNA X.25 DTEs to be connected to non-SNA X.25 DTEs by permanent virtual circuit services or virtual call services, or both.

USE OF X.25 FOR SNA-TO-SNA CONNECTIONS

SNA defines a layered structure for communication networks that enables network end users, such as operators and application programs, to communicate without regard for the operational details of the telecommunications media and data transmission services employed.

The information transmitted between end users in an SNA network may traverse several data links and intermediate nodes. Each pair of nodes directly connected by a data link is termed 'adjacent' within SNA. The data link control (DLC) elements provide the lowest level of management for data transmission between the adjacent nodes. In addition to its data transmission function, the DLC also handles other tasks such as initialisation, identification exchange, and link tests between adjacent nodes.

These adjacent node functions are readily implemented over point-to-point and multipoint links, in which one station acts in a control or primary role and the other stations act as secondaries. (Since secondary stations on a multipoint circuit cannot communicate directly with one another, they are not adjacent in the SNA sense.) When a public packet-switched data network serves as the medium connecting SNA nodes, the requirement for adjacent node functions still exists, but the actual physical adjacency is absent.

To permit concurrent use of data link control and virtual circuit protocol services, all of the properties of the former must be available in the latter. SNA X.25 DTEs employ a Logical Link Control (LLC) protocol to provide certain adjacent node services in environments where SNA nodes are connected through one or more packet networks. This protocol, known as Qualified Logical Link Control (QLLC), uses 'qualified' data packets to transfer data link control information between the

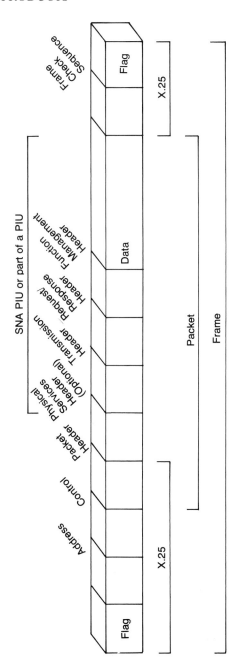

Figure A7.1   Packet and Frame Formats

two SNA nodes. Once data link connectivity has been established, SNA Path Information Units (PIUs) are transferred in normal, unqualified data packets.

PIUs that exceed the maximum user data area of the data packet are transferred as packet sequences concatenated by the More Data Mark (M bit).

Figure A7.1 shows the format of the frame and included packet for SNA-to-SNA virtual 'rcuits. The frame carries either link-control information only or coural information and a single packet associated with a particular virtual circuit.

USE OF X.25 FOR SNA-TO-NON-SNA CONNECTIONS

The X.25 interface can be used in SNA nodes to make connections to non-SNA nodes through packet-switched data networks. SNA-to-non-SNA connections provide a mechanism for transporting data between an application program that resides in an SNA node and a remote non-SNA terminal, such as a non-SNA X.25 DTE or a start/stop terminal attached to a PAD facility. The three types of operation defined for SNA-to-non-SNA connections are mapped, transparent, and hybrid. No standard protocol is provided above the packet level of Recommendation X.25 for SNA-to-non-SNA connections. These higher-level protocols remain a matter to be agreed upon between the individual non-SNA terminal and the supporting customer-supplied application program within the SNA node.

In mapped operation, all of the X.25 protocols can be mapped to and from similar SNA protocol subsets directly at the SNA X.25 DTE/DCE interface; thus, virtual circuits are associated with SNA sessions on a one-to-one basis. An application in the host can therefore communicate with the non-SNA node without any X.25 sensitivity. However, the application and the remote node must have a common understanding of the data streams being exchanged and must process them accordingly.

In transparent operation, the packet level of X.25 can be implemented in a host application program. In this case, the packet-level protocols are transported, transparently, within the structure of SNA between the application and the X.25 interface.

In hybrid operation, X.25 packet-level functions are neither fully mapped nor fully transparent. An application does some X.25 functions as in transparent operation; the remaining X.25 functions are performed at the X.25 interface.

X.25 ELEMENTS IN SNA NODES

The elements of X.25 selected for use in SNA nodes at the physical level, link level and packet level are described in this section. SNA-to-SNA and SNA-to-non-SNA connections differ only at the packet level. Therefore, descriptions of the physical level and the link level elements are common to both types of connection.

Physical Level

The physical level employs a duplex transmission facility. During an interim period, some SNA X.25 DTEs support X.21 bis instead of X.21 at the physical level.

IBM X.21 bis implementation for non-switched access conforms to:

— CCITT Recommendation V.24 with V.28 electrical characteristics at speeds of 19.2 Kilobits per second (Kbits/s) and below;

— CCITT Recommendation V.35 at signalling speeds in excess of 19.2 Kbits/s.

Switched-circuit access to packet networks is not supported because essential DTE and DCE identification and characterisation functions are still being defined by the CCITT.

Transmission speed is product-specific; however, all SNA X.25 DTEs support at least one of the X.25 speeds (2.4, 4.8, 9.6, or 48.0 Kbits/s) and some may support one or more additional speeds (eg, 1.2, 19.2, 56.0 and 64.0 Kbits/s).

Link Level

Recommendation X.25 defines a symmetrical link access procedure (LAP) and a balanced link access procedure (LAPB) for use as the link-level element. Except for certain early implementations, SNA X.25 DTEs use only the LAPB procedure.

SNA X.25 DTEs transmit and receive only frames containing a single packet consisting of an integral number of octets and are sequenced using modulo 8 sequence numbering. They employ recovery mechanisms that conform fully with LAPB. Packets transferred across the DTE/DCE interface are contained within the link-level information field.

Packet Level

Packet level types transmitted and received and their uses with the various services are shown in Table A7.1.

These packets are used as described in IBM General Information Manual GA27-3345. Except for certain early implementations, the qualifier bit is set (Q = 1) in data packets to transfer Logical Link Control (LLC) information. Packet sequences are generated using the more-data bit. The delivery confirmation bit (D = 1) in data packets is allowed only on SNA-to-non-SNA connections because SNA has its own end-to-end mechanisms at levels above X.25.

Packet type		Service		
From DCE to DTE	**From DTE to DCE**	**VC**	**PVC**	**I/F**
Call set-up and clearing				
Incoming call	Call request	X		
Call connected	Call accepted	X		
Clear indication	Clear request	X		
DCE clear confirmation	DTE clear confirmation	X		
Data [and interrupt]				
DCE data	DTE data	X	X	
[DCE interrupt]	[DTE interrupt]	[X]	[X]	
[DCE interrupt confirmation]	[DTE interrupt confirmation]	[X]	[X]	
Flow control and reset				
DCE receive ready	DTE receive ready	X	X	
DCE receive not ready	DTE receive not ready	X	X	
Reset indication		X	X	
	Reset request		X	
DCE reset confirmation	DTE reset confirmation		X	
Restart				
Restart indication	Restart indication			X
DCE restart confirmation	DTE restart confirmation			X
Diagnostic*				X

VC = Virtual Call   I/F = Entire DTE/DCE interface
PVC = Permanent Virtual Circuit   [ ] = For SNA-to-non-SNA connections only
*Not necessarily available on all networks
Note: DTE REJECT and DATAGRAM packets are not used

Table A7.1   Packet Types and their Uses with Various Services

Other X.25 data packet characteristics include packet sequence numbering modulo 8 or, optionally, 128; maximum user data fields of 128 or, optionally, additional sizes of 16, 32, 64, 512 or 1024 octets; and window sizes (W), $1 \leqslant W < 8$ of module 8 packet sequence numbering or $1 \leqslant W < 128$ for modulo 128 packet sequence numbering.

In addition to the specific significance specified in X.25 for bits 8 and 7 of the first octet of the user data field in CALL REQUEST and INCOMING CALL packets, the remaining bits of this octet are used to distinguish between SNA-to-SNA and SNA-to-non-SNA connections that may coexist at the same X.25 DTE/DCE interface.

When subscribed optional user facilities are indicated in INCOMING CALL packets, SNA X.25 DTEs do one of the following:

— accept the call with no further negotiation;

— attempt parameter negotiation using the facilities field in the CALL ACCEPTED packet;

— reject the call using the CLEAR REQUEST packet with an appropriate diagnostic indication.

Table A7.2 shows optional user facilities for SNA DTEs.

Some X.25 optional user facilities require that explicit support functions be provided by the DTE; others, designated 'User Choice', do not; they are designated to the packet carrier when the X.25 interface is subscribed.

During the data transfer phase, SNA X.25 DTEs process error notification information contained in RESET, CLEAR, RESTART, or DIAGNOSTIC packets. On SNA-to-SNA connections, all DTEs use a consistent set of diagnostic codes that flow end-to-end as the result of clearing, resetting, or restarting. Whether an error is detected by the DTE or by the DCE, the DTE notifies the SNA higher levels of the error condition so that recovery procedures can be initiated.

IBM X.25 PRODUCT SUPPORT

The X.25 recommendation provides DTE-to-DTE connectivity through a packet-switched network. Additional, higher-level functions are required to accomplish communications. This procedure can be compared to the public switched telephone network that provides the connec-

X.25 optional user facilities provided	IBM SNA X.25 DTEs
Non-standard default window size	All
Default throughput class assignment	User choice
Incoming calls barred	User choice
Outgoing calls barred	User choice
Single closed user group (CUG)	User choice
Single CUG with outgoing access	User choice
Single CUG with incoming access	User choice
Incoming calls barred within a CUG	User choice
Outgoing calls barred within a CUG	User choice
One-way logical channel outgoing	Some
One-way logical channel incoming	Some
Reverse charging	Some
Reverse charging acceptance	Some
Non-standard default packet size	Some
Flow control parameter negotiation	Some
Throughput class negotiation	Some
Multiple closed user groups	Some
Multiple CUG with outgoing access	Some
Multiple CUG with incoming access	Some
Extended packet sequence numbering	Some
RPOA selection	Some
Fast select	Some
Fast select acceptance	Some
Packet retransmission	None
Bilateral closed user group	None
Bilateral CUG with outgoing access	None

All = facilities always provided
Some = facilities that may be optionally provided
None = facilities not normally provided
User choice = facilities provided solely by packet networks

Table A7.2   Optional User Facilities for SNA DTEs

tion, but the parties connected must speak the same language to accomplish communication. SNA in circuit-switched and non-switched environments provides the higher-level communication functions once connectivity is attained.

The IBM product implementations conform to the 1980 CCITT X.25 recommendation subset. Among the X.25 products offered by IBM are the 5973 L02 Network Interface Adapter (NIA), which is an external protocol converter, and the X.25 program product that operates in the

3705 Communications Controller in conjunction with the Network Control Program (NCP). The X.25 program product is called the NCP Packet Switched Interface (NPSI). Other products include X.25 features for the Series/1 processor and the 5251 Data Entry Display. Four different types of packet-switched communication can be described for the IBM products, but not all are supported by each product:

1 SNA-host-to-SNA-peripheral node

2 SNA-host-to-SNA-host/peripheral node

3 SNA-host-to-non-SNA-DTE

4 Non-SNA-processor-to-non-SNA-DTE

SNA-Host-to-SNA-Peripheral Node

The IBM X.25 product offerings make possible several different configurations of this type. One configuration uses the NPSI program product in configuration with the NIA as shown in Figure A7.2.

The NPSI program product places SNA messages into packets. After the packets are transported through the packet-switched data network, the NIA removes the SNA messages from the packets and sends them over an SDLC link to the peripheral node. In this configuration the NIA is referred to as a remote NIA.

In a second configuration for SNA-host-to-SNA-peripheral node communication, another version of the NIA replaces the NPSI program product as shown in Figure A7.3.

Here the NIA is known as the front-end NIA; it can be used to attach an IBM 4331 processor, 8100 processor, 3705-80 controller, System/34, or System/38 to a packet-switched data network. The front-end NIA can communicate through the network to a remote NIA. Each NIA functions as an SDLC/X.25 protocol converter.

Another instance of SNA-host-to-SNA-peripheral node communication occurs using the IBM 5251 Integrated X.25 Attachment or 5294 Remote Control Unit to communicate with a System/34 or System/38 attached to the network using a front-end NIA.

As an alternative to the front NIA arrangement, the System/36 X.25 Attachment Feature (No 5680) and software can be used to support

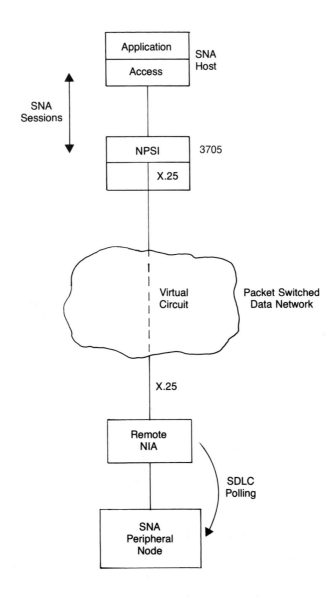

Figure A7.2

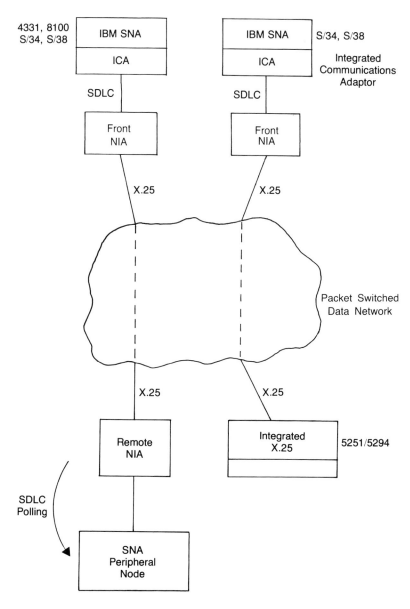

Figure A7.3

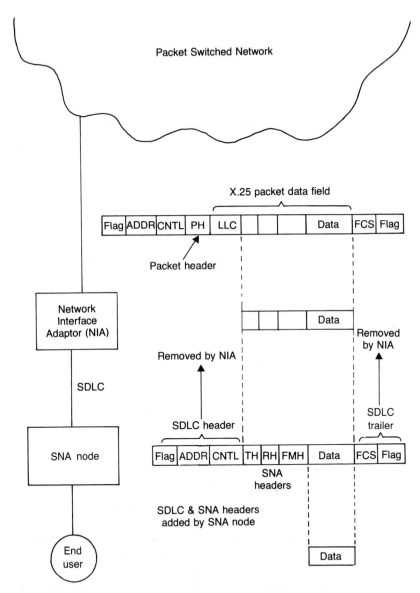

Figure A7.4   Operation of the Network Interface Adaptor

connections of remote workstations attached via an IBM 5294 Remote Control Unit. This feature can also be used to attach System/36s to each other and to System/370 SNA hosts.

Although a remote NIA can control only a single permanent or switched virtual circuit, a front-end NIA can control four permanent virtual circuits or one switched virtual circuit. With either NIA, virtual calls can be initiated from an attached keypad.

In order to avoid sending an excessive number of non-data packets through the network, the host polls the front-end NIA which responds to the host but does not pass the poll to the network. Instead, the front-end NIA lets the remote NIA do the polling of the attached peripheral node.

Figure A7.4 shows how either type of NIA works. Data originating with an end-user is passed to the SNA node where the TH, RH and FMH headers particular to SNA are added by the layers above the data link control layer. The data link control layer, implementing SDLC, adds the frame header and trailer fields and passes the complete frame over a local link to the NIA where the integrity of the frame is checked and the SDLC header and trailer removed. The NIA adds a special header, LLC (logical link control), which is used to provide end-to-end assurance of delivery across the network. The data field, SNA headers and the LLC constitute the X.25 frame data field. X.25 level 2 (ie HDLC) header and trailer are added by the NIA, using some information from the discarded SDLC header, and the complete X.25 frame is transmitted to the local packet switching exchange for transport to the other SNA node.

Although there are some country-by-country restrictions, the list of SNA products attachable to the NPSI and NIAs as of this writing is shown in Table A7.3.

SNA-Host-to-SNA-Host/Peripheral Node

The NPSI (Release 3) program product supports packet switched communication via two 3705 Communications Controllers using X.25 permanent virtual circuits. This support provides the capability of having an application in one host communicating through an X.25 network either to an application in another host or to an application in an X.25 peripheral node attached to the different host or its associated communications controller.

SNA peripheral nodes attachable through remote NIA	SNA host X.25 access				
	NPSI System/370, 303X, 4341, 3081	4331	Front-end NIA		
			8100 System	System /34	System /38
3271	X	X			
3274	X	X	X		
3275	X	X			
3276	X	X	X		
3601, 3602	X	X	X		
3605/5995	X	X			
3651	X	X	X		
3680	X	X	X		
3771, 3774, 3775, 3776, 3777	X	X			
3791/3730	X	X	X		
5251				X	X
5285, 5288	X	X			
Series/1	X	X			
System/32	X	X			
System/34	X	X		X	
System/38	X	X			
8100 System	X	X	X		
8775	X	X	X		

Table A7.3 SNA Peripheral Node Support

SNA-Host-to-Non-SNA-DTE

The NPSI program product can support three types of communication to non-SNA DTEs:

— SNA-host-to-X.25-native DTE;

— SNA-host-to-start/stop-PAD device;

— SNA-host-to-nonstandard-PAD device.

The X.25 interface for SNA-to-SNA and SNA-to-non-SNA communication differs only at the packet level. For SNA-to-non-SNA communication there are no end-to-end SNA formats or protocols. Necessary higher-level protocols must be agreed upon between the individual non-SNA X.25 terminal and the supporting customer-supplied application in the SNA host.

SNA-Host-to-X.25-Native DTE (see Figure A7.5)

Communication between an SNA host and a non-SNA X.25 DTE is
controlled either by a portion of the NPSI program product known as the
Protocol Converter for Non-SNA Equipment (PCNE) or by a user application program in the host. The transformation in the PCNE function
between SNA and X.25 is referred to as a mapped operation in which the
X.25 DTE is represented to SNA as a known peripheral node. The NPSI
maps between X.25 protocols and IBM 3767 keyboard/display protocols,
but no mapping occurs between the X.25 user data field and the SNA
data stream. This is different from the conversion in the NIA, where
SDLC protocols are converted to and from X.25 protocols and the
higher-level, end-to-end protocols are passed through from the host to
the DTE.

The non-SNA equipment may be a terminal or a CPU, as long as it
supports the X.25 interface. This is especially useful when the user wants

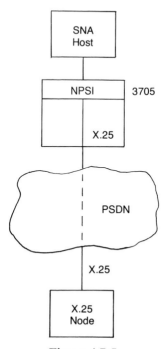

Figure A7.5

to use his own non-SNA protocols between an application program in the SNA network and the non-SNA DTE.

Two additional features of the NPSI program product can be used for communication to an X.25 native DTE. They are the General Access to X.25 Transport Extension (GATE) and the Dedicated Access to X.25 Transport Extension (DATE). 'Transport extension' refers to an extension of the X.25 interface from the NPSI in the 3705 Communications Controller to an application in the host. With GATE and DATE, an application program signals the program product to send certain control packets to activate or deactivate virtual circuits. This allows the user's application to communicate through the network to non-SNA devices. The user defines his own higher level protocols. DATE also can be used to provide SNA-host-to-SNA-peripheral-node communication, with the user providing a program to process X.25 control packets.

GATE and DATE are similar, but in GATE a single application program in the host communicates both control information and data to multiple non-SNA X.25 DTEs. In DATE, there are multiple application programs in the host, one of which is dedicated for communicating only control information. All other application programs using DATE communicate only data packets.

SNA-Host-to-Start/Stop-PAD Device (see Figure A7.6)

Communication between an SNA host and an asynchronous, start/stop DTE (conforming to CCITT Recommendation X.28) is accomplished by using a network-provided PAD. Integrated support in the X.25 NPSI program product allows start/stop terminals to communicate with an SNA host application. The program product controls the PAD using a set of qualified data packet functions defined in CCITT Recommendation X.29.

CCITT Recommendation X.3 defines operation of the network PAD. An X.25 permanent virtual circuit or virtual call connects the NPSI to the PAD. The data transfer protocol must be predefined and understood by both the start/stop terminal and the host application.

SNA-Host-to-Nonstandard-PAD Device (see Figure A7.7)

Some packet-switched data networks support attachment of devices for which CCITT has no recommendations. These include non-SNA devices such as the binary synchronous IBM 3270 display and the IBM 2780 remote job entry system. Since there is no built-in PAD control, an application program must process PAD control information, which is conveyed to the packet-switched network by non-standard PAD support in the NPSI program product.

The NPSI program product also supports a number of other program products (SNA-to-SNA only). These include the following database, time-sharing, and communication network management program products: Customer Information Control System (CICS), Information Management System (IMS), Time Sharing Option (TSO), Network Communications Control Facility (NCCF), and Virtual Storage Personal Computing (VSPC). The Network Terminal Option (NTO) can co-reside with the NPSI program product, which can be used with multiple X.25 interfaces to the same or different packet-switched networks. Multiple

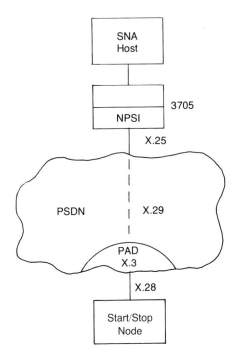

Figure A7.6

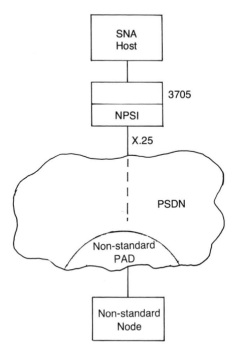

Figure A7.7

interfaces to the same network can be configured to add link capacity for additional users.

Non-SNA-Processor-to-Non-SNA-DTE

The IBM Series/1 processor provides integrated X.25 support for a non-SNA environment. This support manages the X.25 protocols on behalf of a user application program. Applications are written to a macro level interface. The user-supplied application program must support end-to-end protocols above the packet level. An interface is also provided so that user programs can communicate over point-to-point links using LAPB, bypassing the packet level.

SUMMARY

The implementation of the X.25 interface in IBM products provides an additional communication service that can co-reside in SNA nodes with a large array of other communication services, thus allowing the user more flexibility. The X.25 functions used in SNA have been selected based on current user requirements. Future requirements include direct DTE-to-DTE communication without an intervening packet network, and providing the DCE side of the interface in SNA nodes so that an SNA network can provide X.25 packet-switched services.

Appendix 8

Development of CCITT Standards for Packet Data Networks in the Period 1980-1984

INTRODUCTION

The International Telegraph and Telephone Consultative Committee (CCITT) is the data and telecommunications standards body of the International Telecommunications Union (ITU) which, like the International Standards Organisation (ISO), is an agency of the United Nations.

CCITT is responsible for producing Recommendations for telecommunications equipment and services to be applied to public communications networks.

Activities at CCITT are the responsibility of study groups (SGs), and the recommendations they produce are agreed and ratified at the Plenary Assembly every four years. The X-series Recommendations are the responsibility of SG VII, which is concerned with all aspects of data communications networks including the interchange of data over public networks. Each SG entrusts the work to be carried out during the study period to a number of working parties (WPs) of experts in a particular field.

The CCITT/SG VII was entrusted by the VIIth Plenary Assembly in 1980 with the study of 41 Questions (items of study) related to data communications networks. SG VII set up five WPs with the following responsibilities:

— WP VII/1: network service classes and facilities;
— WP VII/2: network access interfaces;
— WP VII/3: network interworking, switching and signalling;
— WP VII/4: network transmission and maintenance;
— WP VII/5: network aspects.

In the course of the 1981-1984 period, the SG drew up 35 new recommendations. Substantial amendments have also been made to 25 existing recommendations.

In conclusion, a total of 71 recommendations have been contained in the X-series for data communication networks.

With regard to the proposed study programme for the next study period, 1985-1988, SG VII will retain a number of existing Questions and add 22 new Questions, making a total of 48. Most of the new Questions relate to interworking, including the ISDN, and to message presentation services including directories, document architectures and message-handling systems.

EVOLUTION OF X.25

The X.25 Recommendation was firmly established in 1980 as a workable interface specification for packet mode data terminal equipment (DTE). Its adoption internationally by all packet-switched public data networks (PSPDNs) has helped considerably towards its stability as an interface for worldwide communication. The question of stability was also paramount in the minds of the SG VII/WP2 participants collaborating in this work with other standards groups, DTE manufacturers and users, since stability ensures a growing market for the protocol and wider availability of cheaper X.25 terminals.

SG VII/WP2 has been particularly concerned in the last four years with the following main issues:

— the interworking of private X.25 networks with public packet-data networks;
— the alignment of X.25 to provide the open systems interconnection (OSI) network service requirements;
— new optional user facilities particularly the on-line registration and network user identification facilities;
— the readability of X.25 text and its accuracy.

In resolving these issues, it has been ensured that the new capabilities do not impact on existing implementations of terminals or networks. Certain facilities have been upgraded from optional to mandatory status. Table A8.1 lists all the facilities for the switched virtual call service to be made available in all PSPDNs.

Facilities assigned for an agreed period of time	Facilities on a per call basis

Closed user group
Flow control parameters
  negotiation
Throughput class
  negotiation
Fast select acceptance
Incoming calls barred
Outgoing calls barred
One-way logical channel outgoing
	Closed user group selection
	Window size negotiation
	Packet size negotiation
	Fast select
	Throughput class negotiation
	Transit delay selection and
	  indication

Table A8.1   Essential Facilities for Packet Data Networks Applicable to a Virtual Call Service

Interworking with Private Networks

X.25 in 1984 incorporated a number of enhancements to provide the end-to-end control required when interconnecting private X.25 networks to public networks. Currently, there is no explicit international agreement on interworking protocols for private X.25 networks and for local area networks (LANs) operating in the connection-oriented mode and wishing to access wide-area networks. X.25 is naturally suited for such interworking cases. However, a number of other interworking issues still remain to be resolved: those involving multiple connections, methods of routeing when alternative routes are provided in public networks, and security aspects.

Enhancements relate to the exchange of charging information, local charging prevention and closed user groups (CUGs), the latter being extended to a maximum of 10,000 CUGs.

Consideration was also given to the explicit identification of the calling DTE and the PSPDN, the restrictions of X.25 timeouts, the inclusion of call progress signals in call clear, reset and restart packets and call redirection within the private network.

The numbering plan for public networks, X.121, has also been extended to allow addressing and subaddressing capabilities for private networks. As a supplement, and specifically for OSI, the network address extension facility was incorporated in X.25.

Alignment with the OSI Network Service

It has been decided by CCITT and ISO that the X.25 virtual call service protocol will be used to provide the OSI connection-oriented network service described in Appendix 6.

Towards this end, certain elements and procedures were added to X.25 and new facilities were introduced.

Optional User Facilities

Fast Select and Fast Select Acceptance were upgraded to essential facilities. These now permit user data of up to 128 octets in call confirmation and clear packets.

The Transit Delay Selection and Indication facility was also introduced as an essential facility. This enables a DTE to specify a desired transit delay on a per call basis, and the network is requested to allocate resources and to route a call in such a manner that the requested transit delay indicated to the DTEs is not exceeded.

CCITT-Specified DTE Facilities

The facilities intended to support end-to-end signalling required by the OSI Network service are carried transparently end-to-end between DTEs and are contained in the facility field under a new marker – the CCITT-specified DTE facilities marker.

The Calling and Called Address Extension capability, which operates beyond the 14 digit maximum address that identifies a DTE connected to a public network (as defined in X.121), permits calling and called addresses of up to 32 digits (16 octets) each to be transferred in call set-up and clear packets.

The Quality of Service negotiation facilities are the end-to-end transit delay (cumulative, requested, maximum acceptable) negotiation facility, the expedited data negotiation facility and the minimum throughput class negotiation facility.

Other changes to support the OSI network service involve the extension of the interrupt packet user data from 1 octet to the 32 octet maximum required by the expedited service, the agreement that the general format-identifier field will provide the means of protocol identification to be used at the network layer and the negotiation of the overall availability of the D bit to support the Receipt Confirmation service.

Changes to the Link Level

The X.21 bis interface is no longer an interim solution, as in 1980, and it has equal status to the X.21 interface for connections to PSPDNs.

The link-layer access protocol (LAPB) has been aligned with the single-link procedures of X.75. Multilink procedures were also introduced into the LAPB. These operate over multiple physical connections between a single DTE and a node on the PSPDN (see Figure A8.1(a)). These connections are viewed as a single logical link, and data packets are interchanged independently across these connections. Multilink procedures provide resequencing of frames for optimüim load-sharing, and links can be added or removed without the loss of data packets or the need for calls to be cleared. Figure A8.1(b) illustrates the model for multilink procedures.

The extended numbering option, modulo 128, for frame-sequencing over satellite links, for example, was also introduced in LAPB.

Facilities and Enhancement to the Packet Level

The datagram service has been deleted in the X.25 and X.2 Recommendations, since no PTT or network administration is currently planning to provide this service. A question that more accurately reflects the emerging area of interest in connectionless services was set for further study.

An optional facility, on-line registration, was introduced to allow a DTE to request registration of facilities or to obtain current values of facilities offered by the PSPDN. Some facilities, such as flow-control parameters, charging information, etc, can be negotiated, while others, eg CUGs, are not indicated by the network. Dynamic changes of facility options by means of the on-line registration procedure prior to setting up a call are also useful for X.25 switched access (X.32) described later.

An optional security feature, the local-charging prevention facility, was introduced which, if subscribed to, authorises the network to prevent a customer from receiving reverse-charge calls or third-party charges and from making chargeable calls.

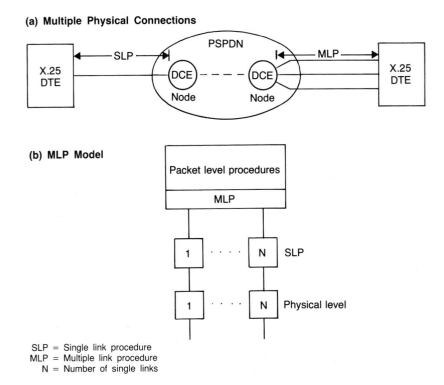

SLP = Single link procedure
MLP = Multiple link procedure
  N = Number of single links

Figure A8.1   Single and Multilink Connections to X.25 DTEs

The Network User Identification (NUI) facility enables a DTE to provide information for billing, security or management purposes when setting up a call to the PDN.

The Charging Information facility provides call data (duration, segment count) to the subscriber to this facility when the call is cleared.

When subscribed to, the Call Redirection facility permits calls to a busy or out-of-order DTE to be routed to another DTE. In addition, a Call-Redirection Notification facility can be used to inform the alternative DTE of the reason for call redirection and the address of the original DTE.

The Hunt-group facility is used when there are a number of DTEs connected to the same called address. This facility permits the distribution of incoming calls across the designated group of DTE interfaces.

The Called-Line Address-Modified Notification facility is also new, and it is used to inform the calling DTE, within the call-connected or clear-indication packets, that the call has been redirected and to which DTE address it has been sent.

The CUG facility now covers an extensive number of variants. A CUG with an outgoing access-selection facility, to be used for called DTEs that are connected to large, private networks, was also introduced.

The permissible packet sizes were increased to 2,048 octets and 4,096 octets.

The facility field length was also increased to 109 octets (from 64) to accommodate the new facility codes, including those for OSI. Thus, for universal operation, all networks are required to offer a maximum packet length (call request) of 259 octets, including the link-level fields.

The Recognised Private Operating Agency (RPOA) facility was also extended to allow a DTE to select more than one RPOA transit network.

EMERGENCE OF X.32

The need to provide access to packet data networks through other public switched networks and, in particular, the telephone network (PSTN) and the circuit-switched data networks (CSPDN) was first discussed at CCITT at the Hague, Netherlands, in March 1982.

By the end of 1984, a new, but incomplete, draft recommendation X.32 emerged to describe the functional elements of the interface to PSPDN services for dial-up access. This interface supports packet-mode DTEs and teletex terminals.

The procedural aspects for both dial-in and dial-out operations have also been studied but have not been finalised for publication (Figure A8.2).

PSPDNs can offer two main types of service when accessed by X.25 DTEs via switched networks. These services depend on whether the DTE has been previously registered with the PSPDN. Terminals that have a leased-line connection and have made prior arrangements regarding facilities, number of logical channels, etc might wish to use dial-up access as a back-up service. On the other hand, DTEs unknown to the PSPDN, eg mobile DTE users for whom a dedicated access line is not economically justified, might wish to make temporary use of the PSPDN

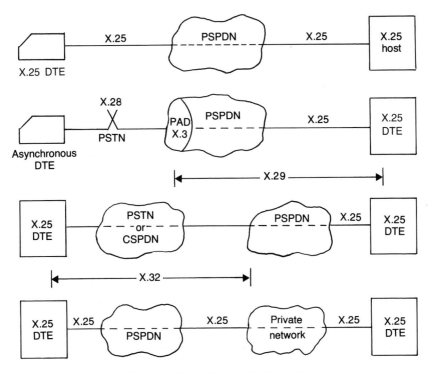

Figure A8.2   Protocol Scenarios

services via the PSTN or CSPDN. In that case, a PSPDN can offer a limited number of facilities, ie, those optimal user facilities that govern the direction of virtual-call placement, or even an extended set of user facilities with certain restrictions in the lifetime of the switched-access path.

X.32 is very much concerned with the problem of identification of terminals, the authentication of access to the network in dial-in operations and, conversely, the identification of the network to enable a DTE to operate, for example, with the correct CUG. The identification protocol, therefore, allows the exchange of specific security-related information (eg encrypted key, signature, etc) for authentication of access to optional user facilities and services.

X.32 outlines several means of identification, some of which may be complementary:

- no identification of the caller, therefore no chargeable calls or reverse charge calls are permitted. This means that limited facilities are offered and methods of charging are arranged otherwise;
- identification by means of the PSTN or CSPDN calling-line identification signal: this is a secure method used widely for charging purposes, but it does not guarantee the actual identity of the caller;
- identification by means of procedures prior to a virtual call: these involve exchanges of exchange identification (XID) frames or registration packets;
- identification on a per-call basis by means of the NUI facility which may contain information for billing or security purposes.

It is anticipated that dial-up access using X.32 will become an important service in the future. Network providers in France, Canada and the UK already support some form of switched access to subscribed X.25 DTEs. For example in the UK, the InterStream Two service provides Teletex message transfer between the PSTN and PSS. X.32, as it does not need a dedicated line, would reduce the cost of X.25 access, thus encouraging its implementation on smaller systems and on the external gateways of simple LANs that require occasional access to PSPDN services.

FURTHER ENHANCEMENTS OF THE PACKET ASSEMBLY/ DISASSEMBLY FACILITY

Support of interactive, asynchronous, start/stop mode terminals (DTE-Cs) accessing packet networks is provided by the three CCITT Recommendations X.3, X.28 and X.29, which are known collectively as 'Triple X'. The connection of these terminals to PSPDNs is accomplished via a packet assembly/disassembly (PAD) facility which typically supports a number of DTE-Cs simultaneously.

The demand for advanced facilities in the PAD to support the sophisticated features of intelligent terminals that are available has increased considerably in the last four years. Examples of these facilities include editing, line-feed insertion, parity checking and insertion, selective editing and call reselection. Certain features required to enhance the user friendliness of the PAD interface have also been introduced in the signalling protocol.

Four new functions have been introduced in the 1984 Triple X:

— Editing PAD service signals (parameter 19): this controls the format of the editing service signals sent to the DTE-C by the PAD depending on the type of terminals, namely, a printer or a visual display;

— Echo mask (parameter 20): if the echo function is enabled, then received characters will be echoed to th DTE-C prior to the transmission of any data waiting at the PAD; parameter 20 permits the terminal user to control which group of characters is echoed back by the PAD;

— Parity treatment by the PAD (parameter 21): the PAD can now check the parity of the data received from the terminal and/or generate parity of the data transmitted to the terminal; the type of parity (even, odd, mark, space) is indicated by the eighth bit of the character received by the PAD; if there is a parity error, the PAD will return an error-service signal and not echo the character in error;

— Page wait (parameter 22): the PAD can be directed by the DTE-C to suspend the transmission of data to it after a specified number of lines were transmitted; the PAD can resume the transmission of data when, for example, it receives an X-ON character from the DTE-C; this type of operation is intended for VDU terminals that might be receiving a large volume of data.

An extensive number of minor changes and improvements were also introduced; these, however, will not affect terminal equipment implementations:

— Reselection: by means of X.29 procedures, the PAD can be requested to clear a call and establish a new virtual call to a reselected X.25 DTE; for this purpose, the packet mode DTE provides all the information required in the incoming call-packet to the reselected X.25 DTE; this facility is optional;

— New access rates of 1200 bits/s duplex and 1200/75 bits/s were introduced;

— PAD service signals can now be specified in a network-dependent format;

— The maximum length of X.29 PAD messages was set to 128 octets, and error reports in X.29 from the PAD were improved;

— National or local parameters not standardised in X.3 can be indicated in PAD messages; their use is not recommended for international or internetwork communications;

— All facilities planned to be supported by the PAD have been allocated a specific code;

— PAD to PAD signalling on receipt of a 'break' has been improved;

— A PAD now provides explicit support of the D bit; there is no guarantee of data delivery to the DTE-C being implied, however, from the acknowledgement sent by the PAD to the packet-mode DTE;

— Parameter indication PAD messages carry error-codes for invalid attempts to adjust parameters.

IMPACT OF OSI

CCITT and ISO have well-established links of cooperation in many areas. Their cooperative effort to develop a common version of the OSI Reference model has, however, been unprecedented. This has given extra impetus to the model as an international standard. The technical alignment of the models described in X.200 and IS7498 was achieved early in the CCITT cycle.

The OSI model description (see Appendix 6) consists of an abstract hierarchy of seven layers of services/protocols, and lists, in broad terms, the principle functions of each layer.

Table A8.2 lists the CCITT recommendations developed for OSI and the equivalent ISO documents. These relate to the connection-oriented services and protocols and to the services offered by PTTs such as teletex (advanced telex), videotex (text transmission) and message handling.

Network Layer Protocols

For PDNs conforming to X.25, the connection-oriented network service (NS) has achieved complete technical alignment with the switched, virtual-circuit service. The OSI NS offers a set of mandatory features that are globally provided, and the two optional services of receipt confirmation and expedited data-transfer are facilitated in X.25 by means of the D bit and interrupt packet, respectively.

The functional characteristics of a connection between two end-users across one or more real networks is expressed by a set of quality of service

CCITT	ISO	Title
X.200	IS 7498	Basic reference model
X.210	DP 8509	Service definition conventions
X.213	DIS 8348	Network layer service
X.214	DIS 8072	Transport layer service
X.215	DIS 8326	Session layer service
X.224	DIS 8073	Transport layer protocol
X.225	DIS 8327	Session layer protocol
X.25	DIS 7776	Link-layer access protocol (LAPB)
X.25	DIS 7478	Link-layer multilink protocol (MLP)
X.25	DIS 8208	Network layer protocol

IS = international standard; DIS = draft international standard; DP = draft proposal

Table A8.2   Standards Relating to OSI for Connection-Oriented Services and Protocols

(QOS) parameters, which include throughput and transit delay referred to earlier, and network connection priority.

Network connection priority relates to the occasional congestion problems that arise in packet networks. It enables a connection that supports a number of applications to be degraded or discarded as a result of this congestion. Priority is expressed by three subparameters:

— priority to obtain a network connection, for example, in order to obtain diagnostic information regarding the congestion;
— priority to hold and keep a connection until the completion of certain data transfers;
— priority for certain types of data traffic over, for example, queued data traffic.

Other parameters such as acceptable cost, residual error rates, etc are also important considerations related to routeing, management and maintenance of the network connection.

Network Layer Addressing

The subject of global addressing for the unambiguous identification of any terminal in the open systems environment has been the most controversial and difficult to define and resolve. By 1984, certain agreements were reached between ISO and CCITT, on the basis of which a network layer addressing scheme was progressed. This scheme relies on the concept of the network service access point (NSAP), which is the interface address between the network layer and the transport layer of the OSI model. In addition, some progress was made towards establishing an international registration authority to control and administer the allocation of NSAP addresses, in a similar manner to the way in which CCITT administers data network identification codes (DNICs) to public networks.

Existing numbering plans such as X.121, F.69, E.163, etc, as defined by CCITT for public networks, are considered inadequate for OSI addressing. They exclude private networks and LANs that do not attach to public networks and terminals on a private network, which can have more than one address assigned to them if that private network is attached to one or more public networks. Furthermore, current interworking arrangements for the routeing of calls through concatenated networks are complex and in most cases undeveloped.

On the basis that any addressing solution agreed to by CCITT and ISO must utilise existing networks without changing their individual addressing schemes or internal routeing implementations, the worldwide OSI numbering plan has set as its main principle the preservation of existing allocations of DNICs, for example, to public packet data networks. In general, NSAPs can only be identified by addressing information offered by the NS user in addition to that required by the point of attachment to a real network. As an example, X.25-based networks would be required to carry across two address fields in the call request packet. One would be for the network address of up to 14 digits, in accordance with X.121, and would define the specific DTE/DCE interface at the attachment to the PSPDN, and the other would be for the NSAP address, which would appear in a facility field as a separate entity under the CCITT-specified DTE facility marker. This mechanism requires no action to be taken by packet data networks and no directory function to support the OSI systems on such networks is necessary. What is required is the implementation of enhancement mechanisms by end-users and public or private gateways.

ACKNOWLEDGEMENT

Acknowledgement is made to the Head of Division, National Packet Switching Services, British Telecom, UK for permission to publish this paper.

CCITT RECOMMENDATIONS

CCITT, Red book, Volume VIII, Fascicle VII.2. X.1 Recommendation. 'International user classes of services in public data networks and Integrated service digital networks'. This details the categories of data transmission services in which the signalling rate, call-control signalling rate and DTE modes are standardised.
CCITT, Red book, Volume VIII, Fascicle VIII.2. X.10 Recommendation. 'Category of access for DTEs to public data transmission services provided by PDNs and/or ISDNs through terminal adaptors'. This defines the different categories of access for DTEs to circuit-switched, packet-switched and leased-circuit data-transmission services.
CCITT, Red book, Volume VIII, Fascicle VIII.4. X.121 Recommendation. 'International numbering plan for public data networks'. The X.121 scheme permits identification of a country, a specific PDN in that country and the address of the PDN user.
CCITT, Red book, Volume II, Fascicle II.2. E.163 Recommendation. 'Numbering plan for the international telephone service'. This recommendation assigns a code to each country and permits the identification of a country area for the purpose of routeing calls or identifying services, and the subscriber (local) number.
CCITT, Red book, Volume II, Fascicle II.4. F.69 Recommendation. 'Plan for telex destination codes'. This lists the telex destination and telex network identification codes.
The X-Series Recommendations – Volume VIII – are soon to be published in the Red book (they may be ordered from CCITT, Sales Services, ITU, Place des Nations, CHJ1211, Geneva 20, Switzerland). Volume VIII consists of the following seven fascicles:

— VIII.1 – Data communication over the telephone network. Series V Recommendations.
— VIII.2 – Data communication networks: services and facilities. Recommendations X.1-X.15.
— VIII.3 – Data communication networks: interfaces. Recommendations X.20-X.32.

— VIII.4 – Data communication networks: transmission, signalling and switching, network aspects, maintenance and administrative arrangements. Recommendations X.40-X.181.

— VIII.5 – Data communication networks: Open Systems Interconnection (OSI), system description techniques. Recommendations X.200-X.250.

— VIII.6 – Data communication networks: interworking between networks, mobile data transmission systems. Recommendations X.300-X.353.

— VIII.7 – Data communication networks: message handling systems. Recommendations X.400-X.430.

Appendix 9

Design Notes for PAD Implementors

These *Design Notes for PAD Implementors* were produced by The Character Terminal Implementors Group of British Telecom's New Networks Technical Forum in March 1984.

Contents:

Copies are available from:

The Editor
Dr R G Blake
Programming Manager
Computing Service
University of Essex
Wivenhoe Park
Essex

Index